# Laughing Star

## A story of tough love

*A real-life story by Jo Nisbet, Undiscovered Authors National Non-Fiction Winner.*

# Laughing Star

*A story of tough love*

By
Jo Nisbet

First edition published in Great Britain in 2006
by Discovered Authors Diamonds

A Discovered Authors Diamond
from
Alter-Ego Press

ISBN13 978-1-905108-29-9

Printed in the UK by BookForce

BookForce UK's policy is to use papers that are natural, renewable and
recyclable products and made from wood grown in sustainable forests
where ever possible

BookForce UK Ltd.
50 Albemarle Street
London W1S 4BD
www.bookforce.co.uk
www.discoveredauthors.co.uk

## Acknowledgements

*For my family, friends and neighbours and all those who supported me on this journey into the Abyss and back.*

*For Emily –*

*My 'Laughing Star'*

This is a poem with a theme that runs throughout my life. When I was younger I thought it was all about choices and taking responsibility for the path you take. But as I grew older I began to realise that the path you are on is not always the one you chose. Who and what you are, and what made you who you are governs your journey and whatever path you find yourself on, you take yourself with you.

In 1996, while we were living in Washington, DC, Emily gave me a copy of *'Frost, Collected Poems, Prose and Plays'* for Christmas.

*The Road Not Taken,*
*By Robert Frost*

*Two roads diverged in a yellow wood,*
*And sorry I could not travel both*
*And be one traveller, long I stood*
*And looked down on as far as I could*
*To where it bent in the undergrowth;*

*Then took the other, as just as fair,*
*And having perhaps the better claim,*
*Because it was grassy and wanted wear;*
*Though as for that the passing there*
*Had worn them really about the same,*

*And both that morning equally lay*
*In leaves no step had trodden black.*
*Oh, I kept the first for another day!*
*Yet knowing how way leads on to way,*
*I doubted if I should ever come back.*

*I shall be telling this with a sigh*
*Somewhere ages and ages hence:*
*Two roads diverged in a wood, and I –*
*I took the one less travelled by,*
*And that had made all the difference.*

*'The Road Not Taken'* from The Poetry of Robert Frost edited by Edward Connery Lathem, published by Johnathan Cape. Reprinted by permission of The Random House Group Ltd.

# Prologue

★ ✯ ★

I had reached the point of no return. I felt overwhelmed by the last few months of chaos, confusion, pain - even insanity. There were no more options left to us and I was on automatic pilot – like an oil tanker ploughing through the water towards its destination, completely unable to change direction.

Jonathan came down from Manchester to help me get Emily out of the country and I fixed supper for the three of us in a daze. Tom was, blessedly, in school for the weekend and safely out of the way.

There was very little interaction between us during the meal – nobody felt like eating. I couldn't trust myself to swallow, and the impending conversation hung heavy between us all. Jonathan finally picked the moment to tell Emily that she would be flying to Los Angeles the following day to spend some time with Janette and Bob while we found a new school for her. I don't know what else he could have said; there was no easy way to say: 'Look, you are going to 'Brat Camp' because we can no longer cope with you!'

But Emily was not stupid. She was not going to be taken in by this sop. She shoved her chair back and headed towards the door. Jonathan tried to stop her, and I feared another fight, but she managed to wriggle free and got out of the front door. This time we could not risk her going far. We thought she was likely to go to her friend Olivia, so we called Olivia's parents and explained the seriousness of the situation. Olivia admitted that she knew where Emily would go.

We paced the kitchen, hoping to give Emily time to calm down before calling the number that Olivia had given us. We knew that it was for a house around the corner where she was hiding out with the guy who, only this week, she had referred to as a boyfriend. She was there, but refused to come home. We imposed a midnight deadline and said that if she was not home by then we would ask the police to fetch her.

The deadline came and went, and nobody was answering the phone – I was terrified that they had gone out, or that she had moved on from there. As usual the police were very understanding, and by 3.00 am they were on their way to get her. We needed to be at the airport by 10.30 the next morning for a midday flight.

To distract myself, I threw things into cases so that all we would have to do was fall out of bed and into the car in the morning. Finally, the police arrived. They had had to threaten to break down the door before Emily agreed to come quietly, but now, thank God, she was back under our roof.

I don't remember much about the rest of the night. I can't imagine that either of us slept as we were both on total red alert in case she tried to make another escape – using her old route out of her bedroom window, across the roof, down into the back garden, over the gate and off. We both felt that this might be our last chance to get Emily the help she needed. We couldn't afford to miss this plane.

Eventually dawn arrived and we woke Emily with the intention of arriving at the airport early. She refused to get up. We tried to remain calm; keeping our voices even, but it made no difference. She quickly spiraled into a rage of defiance and this time her anger took me with her.

There was nothing on God's earth that was going to stop me getting her onto that plane, there was too much at stake. I tried to keep my cool, but gradually found myself losing it. By now she was totally defiant, screaming and shouting. I dragged her out of bed, planning to force her to get dressed, but she fought her way past me and into the bathroom, locking the door.

Jonathan tried to reason with her, talking in measured tones through the bathroom door: 'Sweetie, Darling...'. His conciliatory tone was totally ineffectual and, as time leaked away, I found I could no longer keep a lid on my emotions. He pointed out that there was no way we could physically force her onto a plane, so he would have to cancel our flights. But I was not prepared to give up. This fourteen-year-old girl was wrecking her life, and ours. Drugs and alcohol were her escape from reality and, if we gave into her now, what hope would there be for any of us in the future?

Even if her father was willing to give in to this tyrant of a daughter, I was not. I went down to the garage and hunted out tools, intent on unscrewing the lock on the bathroom door. As I wrestled with a screwdriver Emily threatened to kill herself if we got in. I genuinely suspected that she might try. There was no telling anymore what she might be prepared to do.

Having failed with the screwdriver, I returned to the garage in search of a hammer, with the idea of smashing through the door. Jonathan could see that I was losing it – the whole situation must have been very frightening for him. Months later he claimed that I had threatened to smash Emily's head in. Mad as I was at that moment, I know that I could never have done that; but I had passed beyond all normal boundaries.

I was furious that, yet again, he was prepared to give in to her. His attitude seemed totally pathetic to me. All the emotions of the last few months were now bubbling to the surface – I felt like a volcano ready to erupt. Yet if I allowed that to happen I would surely lose all reason. I have no idea just what I would have been capable of doing.

I was so angry that I tried to break down the bathroom door, screaming at Jonathan to: 'Bloody well pull yourself together and **do** something'. I had barely broken one panel in the door before he took over and kicked it in. On the other side of the door, Emily was screaming with fury and promising that she would throw herself out of the window. As the door splintered, Jonathan grabbed her and pulled her out onto the landing. He held her there on the carpet, hoping her anger would subside. As if ...!

My head pounding, and my heart breaking with the anguish of it all, I left them on the landing and put bags into the car. Outside on the driveway I became aware that golfers, arriving at the clubhouse opposite for their Saturday morning game of golf, must be hearing everything that was happening in our house. I suddenly felt very exposed.

How we got Emily to the airport I will never know and, once there, it was only with the fantastic support of Virgin Atlantic security that we managed to coerce her onto the plane. The threat of the indignity of strapping her into a wheelchair in her pyjamas worked in our favour.

Having fought like an animal with my out-of-control daughter I had, this time, won a physical battle. The two of us were now on our way to Los Angeles. But I knew that this skirmish was only a tiny part of the war. No matter how determined I was to save her, Emily was equally determined to self-destruct. Even though I was prepared to do anything to rescue my daughter I understood that the powers of any parent are severely restricted by the life paths that their children choose. You can only stand by, impotent, as they shoot themselves down in flames, while you pray that they will be given some moment of redemption that they will grasp with all their strength.

But, in the heat of the moment, you cannot be sure that this will happen. How can you tell what an out-of-control fourteen-year-old will do?

Teenagers are scarcely more than children, who have rushed into thinking that they are adults. Society tells them that they have a great future, but they don't know what that means, and they don't understand the responsibility of it all. They subscribe readily to the celebrity culture that is inflicted on them, and lose sight of what life is about and what it expects of them. They are lost to the value of their parents' experiences of life and are in danger of never learning how to live, how to give of themselves to make life better. They become stuck in a cycle of self-gratification, with a complete lack of commitment to developing their own lives.

I sat back in my seat on the plane, suspended over the Atlantic Ocean. I felt all used up, totally blown away by the events of the morning. The next hurdle would be getting her through US customs at LAX (Los Angeles Airport), nine hours from now.

# Introduction

★ ☆ ★

I am not a writer, I am an ordinary person – and a wife and a mother. But I have had an experience, which I want to share.

This is a very personal and private story, which I began to write down as a way of recording what happened to us as a family. I hoped that this would help me to work through some intensely difficult problems that confronted us in our efforts to bring up a rather extraordinary child. It started out as a way of moving on, a way of laying ghosts to rest, and an attempt to resolve the many difficulties that we have had to deal with.

Jonathan and I have two children who have been diagnosed with ADHD (Attention Deficit Hyperactive Disorder). They are not defective children – just different children. Society has been harsh in its treatment of them, and severely judgemental of our attempts to bring them up to live full and rich lives. But we believe that they are quite special, and that they deserve the best that we can give them, so that they can fulfil themselves in this world and lead happy lives. We have made many mistakes, some of them serious. There is no manual for bringing up children, let alone different children, but we have tried our best. Most important of all, we cannot help but love them.

Emily, our first born, has taken us to the very edge of our selves. She has tested every limit and every inch of our love. This story is about what happened to her, and to me, her mother who, in throwing everything she had at a daughter who chose a path of self-destruction, almost lost herself and destroyed her family.

With the help of Emily's journals, I am telling this story from my own perspective. I am not trying to tell Jonathan's story, as that is his own to tell. We will have different perceptions of what has happened to us and I am not trying to judge how each of us has behaved. I am simply writing directly from my memory of how things were for me. No one person is to blame for what happened, we each played our part and we must each take responsibility for what we did.

There is very little help or understanding available for families like ours and if, by telling our tale, one other family will not suffer as we did, then it will have been worth it.

# Part one – Into the Abyss

From: THE PROPHET

*And he said:*

*Your children are not your children.*
*They are the sons and daughters of Life's longing for itself.*
*They come through you but not from you,*
*And though they are with you yet they belong not to you.*

*You may give them your love but not your thoughts,*
*For they have their own thoughts.*
*You may house their bodies but not their souls,*
*For their souls dwell in the house of tomorrow, which you cannot visit, not*
*even in your dreams.*
*You may strive to be like them, but seek not to make them like you.*
*For life goes not backward nor tarries with yesterday.*

*You are the bows from which your children as living arrows are sent forth.*
*The archer sees the mark upon the path of the infinite, and He bends you*
*with His might that His arrows may go swift and far.*
*Let your bending in the Archer's hand be for gladness;*
*For even as He loves the arrow that flies, so He loves also the bow that is*
*stable.*

by Kahil Gibran

# Chapter 1

I awoke with a start and lay rigid in my bed. The gentle hum of the air-conditioning unit drowned the sounds of the night outside. The clock on the telephone by the bed stated that it was 3.38 am. It was nearly time. I felt a wave of panic rise up within me and fought to control the shaking, heart-pounding, and gut-wrenching feeling of despair which threatened to overwhelm me. 'Calm down, get a grip', I said to myself. 'You have to get through this. Falling apart now won't do any good at all.'

As I lay there, sweating and afraid, I heard footsteps and a gentle knock on the door.
'Thanks, Bob. I'm awake', I said.

I listened, straining for the sound of an approaching car. Nothing. Pulling on yesterday's shorts and sweatshirt that lay in a heap by the bed, I stumbled into the bathroom, splashed water across my face and drank huge gulps from the tap. Turning on the light I caught a glimpse of myself in the bathroom mirror. Haggard and hollow-eyed, with a nervous rash on my chin – not a pretty sight. I felt a wave of nausea rush over me. I swallowed hard and closed my eyes against it.

Padding barefoot through the kitchen and across the marbled

hallway I thought I heard the sound of a car engine. I looked up at the galleried landing. Emily's door was closed. Bob and Janette tiptoed down the staircase and joined me, just as we heard footsteps beyond the front door. Bob let them in.

Officer Nicholson and his wife, Cheryl, were calm and businesslike. Together we went up the stairs to the landing. Officer Nicholson stood guard at the top of the stairway while Cheryl and I went to Emily's door. Before we went in she said:
'Just wake her gently and tell her that it's time to go. Tell her that she can choose to go quietly, or we will have to use the handcuffs. I will have to watch her get dressed and go to the bathroom but, as much as possible, I will try to have respect for her privacy.'

I stroked Emily's forehead and roused her from a deep sleep.
'You need to wake up, darling, you are going to Utah today, now. They have come to collect you to take you to the Redcliff Ascent programme. This lady's name is Cheryl and she and her husband are here waiting for you to get ready. So, up you get. I will stay with you'.

Emily lay in the darkness, eyes staring. For a moment I thought she would lose it and start shouting but she seemed to change her mind and instead got out of bed and headed for the bathroom.

'Emily, I have to be with you at all times,' said Cheryl gently. 'I'm sure you understand that I cannot let you out of my sight.' She posted herself firmly in the bathroom doorway.

I waited on the landing while Emily threw on jeans and a sweater and followed as Officer Nicholson and Cheryl took her down the stairs between them to the front door. Tears were streaming down her face but she was calm and silent. She let me hug her and I told her that I love her, and that she would be in my thoughts every minute that she is away. And then she was gone.

Stunned, I stood and watched the car pull away. It had all been so quick. So few words spoken. There seemed to be so much to say, and yet nothing left to say. The result was a sort of heavy silence and the darkness of the night, oppressive and humid. I could almost persuade myself that it had just been a scene played through my mind in some kind of sick daydream. That I could change any bit of it at will and rerun it with a different outcome. But I couldn't. I had let two strangers come into the house and take my fourteen-year-old daughter away. I didn't know how long it would be before I would see her again. How could I do this? How had I reached a point where this is the only thing left to do for Emily to help her straighten out her life? What would happen to her? Would she be able to cope? What the hell is this concept of 'tough love' and why must I do it? Why was this happening to us?

I sensed Janette and Bob behind me. I shivered and turned. Gradually I allowed myself to dissolve into tears and just let them hug me like a little child. The enormity of what I had done seemed too much to bear and I simply could not control myself any longer.

We sat up for what remained of the night. Talking and drinking hot tea while I let my dearest friends, Janette and Bob, remind me why I had sent my lovely daughter to 'boot camp' and what made this the best thing to do for Emily right now. How, when this time had become the past, I would look back and say: 'Thank God I had the courage to do this'.

I shall never forget their warmth, compassion and love that night. We must have covered every conceivable positive outcome to this terrible thing while watching the dawn break over the Calabasas hills behind the house and waiting for the phone to ring.

Every hour Officer Nicholson reported on their progress. In the first call they had reached the airport in Los Angeles, where they had boarded the plane for Las Vegas. Then they had landed at Las Vegas airport and were heading off towards St George, Utah, and finally to their destination, the Redcliff Ascent field office at Enterprise. At 10.00 am the Nicholsons signed off. They had delivered Emily safely to the Redcliff Ascent Programme, together with her passport, and a letter from me explaining why I had

done this terrifying thing to her and that it was because I love
her.

# Chapter 2

There had been a series of programmes on Channel 4 television in England three months before about a group of teenage 'brats' who had lost control of their lives and were sent on an outward-bound type therapeutic programme to sort themselves out. This involved a lot of hiking about in the wilderness of Utah, in the USA, living rough and learning survival skills. There were plenty of tears and frustration as they worked their way towards team and individual goals, before they were allowed a reunion with their parents and the journey home to start their lives over again. Several friends and family members called me about it, and my stepmother sent me a video recording of one of the programmes. So began this painful and desperate journey into the wilderness.

But what makes a 'brat'? When my fourteen-year-old daughter, Emily, came off the rails, dropped out of school and went on a mission of total self-destruction, I had to look very deep into my soul to try to understand how it could have happened. Was she born that way? Did I not love her enough? What did I do wrong as a parent that caused her to live in such pain and unhappiness that she no longer cared what happened to her? Why did she say she wanted to die? Why could I no longer reach her? Where has all this violence and rage come from? Why does she think it is my fault? How did I cause it?

I never assumed that I would have children. My own family life had been something of a battleground and I was determined never to repeat it. I got on with my life; building a career in Public Relations, developing a busy social life, then marrying Jonathan. After a while the thought of having a child seemed natural and exciting – it would complete us as a couple, and enrich our lives.

I shall never forget the night that Emily was born. It was a stormy summer night and she was quite unwilling to come into the world. But for me it was such an amazing experience. This beautiful, beautiful baby girl. I had never felt such a pure and enveloping sensation of love in my life. I was giddy with joy and pride. She looked so perfect. I felt complete. I had a loving husband; a comfortable home in Hammersmith, London, we both had successful careers and lots of friends. What more could I ever need? We were the perfect family, living a perfect life.

But Emily was far from easy as a baby. She did not like to be cuddled and would scream and scream. She could not be left alone and was unwilling to do things for herself. I must admit I felt relieved to be going back to work, back to normal problems where I knew the solutions. I was lucky that we were able to afford a wonderful nanny who lived with us for three and a half years. Between us, I knew that Angie and I could cope with this very demanding baby.

Looking back, I can now see things that later became major problems. There was too much screaming, too many tantrums, yet there were also days when Emily was strangely quiet. Often we would go to visit other families with babies and within moments of arriving she would be asleep, only to wake and yell as soon as we were on our way home. It was almost as if the event was too much for her to handle and so she would simply switch off.

As she grew, the quiet days became melancholic days and sometimes, during a conversation, she would simply go blank, almost as if she had disappeared, then return later with no memory of what had been said.

Emily's brother, Tom, arrived when she was two and a half years old. A very different child, he was cuddly, warm, loving and happy. He was in and out of everything as soon as he was able and the differences between them made me worry a lot about Emily.

Yet there were also days when she would be so delightful that I would feel that it was all in my imagination. Nevertheless, I started to read books about childhood and parenting, seeking answers, but never really finding any. The books suggested lots of things to try, so I busied myself with these and continued to listen closely to other parents' experiences in the hope that it was all OK after all.

When Emily started school there were clearly issues with how she coped with the classroom situation. She was withdrawn, but egocentric, expecting both teachers and children to always go in her direction rather than her going with them. She began to be disruptive in class and the head teacher questioned whether she was at the right school.

It was around this time that my husband's job meant a move to the States, to Washington, DC, and this gave me an opportunity to rethink how our home life worked. I had to leave my business and we decided that I should be a full-time mother while we were in America. Both children were quite a handful by this time and it would have been hard to find the right kind of childcare in Washington. Actually I was pleased to take a break from work and decided that I would enjoy being the perfect mother and wife for a while.

Almost as soon as we arrived in Washington, Jonathan's work took him out of state during the week so that he was only home at weekends. This left me to settle the children in schools and to make our rented house, a lovely, traditional, colonial house just north of Washington Cathedral, into a home. I loved living there and quickly made friends and created a life for us all.

I had lots of time to spend with the children and began to realise just how demanding Emily was. Her tantrums were becoming increasingly wild — almost as if she just totally lost control of herself. Nothing I did seemed to help break her spiralling rages.

Teachers at her school started to treat me with suspicion, questioning why she was unwilling to participate in classroom activities. She became less capable, unwilling to write and refusing to read. Being firm, even angry, had no effect; she just switched off. I began to dread going to school to collect her — there was always some issue, or else I would sense the other parents gossiping. I would park the car and walk towards the huddle of mothers waiting outside the door. Invariably their conversation would stop and be replaced by an awkward silence as I joined them.

There was one important exception, my 'Buddy Parent', Elaine — a wonderful person who became a close friend, and who held my hand through all that was to come. Nevertheless I felt like a leper. The situation became very hard to bear and I was at a loss to understand what was happening. I also began to realise that the other children in the class backed away from Emily and I felt shocked and hurt on her behalf.

By the end of the first half term at her new school I was called in and asked to remove her from the school on the basis that she was impossible to teach, and parents were complaining that she was totally disruptive and upsetting the other children.

I was mortified. How could this be? Yes, she was difficult, but I had not realised that things were so serious. I was also very angry – how dare the school (a Convent school at that) expel my daughter? How could the other parents, supposedly good Catholic families, make such cruel judgements of her and her parents?

I could not fail to notice, however, that all was far from well at home. Emily refused to go upstairs on her own and, in fact, resisted being alone at all. If I went into the garden she would scream for me. She hated me speaking on the telephone and seemed to want me to herself, resenting my spending time with Tom, even when I was only reading his bedtime story. She had always been resistant to being held or stroked yet sometimes, if your attention wavered, she would demand a hug but wouldn't give a genuine hug back. It was hard to connect with her in the relaxed and loving way that I could with Tom.

I told my tale of woe to the administrator at Tom's school and the wonderful Aidan Montessori promised to take her in and look closely to see if anything was going wrong with her developmentally. They were very gentle and understanding with us both, and incredibly loving with her. However, after six weeks they advised that there was indeed something very wrong and referred her for a proper medical and psychological assessment.

The diagnosis was that she was suffering from Attention Deficit Hyperactive Disorder. My immediate reaction was: 'What the hell is that?' I had a lot of finding out to do.

Children with ADHD have difficulties paying attention, tend to act quickly and impulsively without thinking things through, are overactive and have trouble sitting still for lengthy periods. They are frequently poor performers in school because they tend to have difficulties with motivation. They are more likely to suffer from a specific learning disability and are often defiant, angry, hostile, and oppositional in response to the commands of others. They become frustrated easily, have frequent temper tantrums and can be very aggressive.

These children typically have difficulty getting on with other people and their impulsiveness often leads to socially unacceptable behaviours. Their frequent experiences of failure, as well as constant reprimands and criticism from others, generally cause children with ADHD to suffer from poor self-esteem and a sense of low self-worth.

It is currently believed that ADHD is due to an under-stimulation of the brain areas that enable a child to sustain attention, delay impulsive responses, control motor activity, follow rules, maintain motivation, and plan behaviour. Research suggests that such under-stimulation is due to dysfunction or delay in the development of these brain areas. Over-activity could be the body's attempt to stimulate these areas of the brain so that they can pay better attention.

Almost overnight I became absorbed into a world of psychiatrists, psychologists, neurologists and education specialists. The various specialists that we had to see tossed around the labels of 'learning disabilities', 'oppositional defiance disorder', and all manner of behavioural disorders. As part of the diagnostic process there were nights of sleep deprivation prior to hospital tests, ECGs and brain scans. I felt I was drowning in a sea of ignorance and it was only the support of close (but new) friends that kept me afloat. For Emily it must have been a bewildering carousel - up at nights, white coats, wires on her head and body scanning devices which in the US are called 'doughnut' machines.

In some ways the diagnosis of ADHD was a relief. The problems were clearly defined; there was a solution (drugs) and a way forward. But there is no cure. At seven years old Emily was still unable to read or write. Here was an explanation and with it a remedy that would change her life and make her normal.

But I was afraid to take the drugs route. These drugs, it was explained, are psycho stimulants designed to stimulate the brain areas that enable a child to sustain attention, delay impulsive responses, control motor activity and plan behaviour. They allow the child to calm down and relax, they reduce the exhaustion produced by over-activity. I was assured that the drugs are not mind altering, in terms of changing personality.

The problem for me was that I could not see how taking medication would teach Emily any skills. Also, what of the side-effects? How would taking a stimulant help with her difficulties in sleeping? Would she become addicted? After all, what is the difference between Methylphenidate and cocaine? Everything was happening too quickly and I did not feel confident that I fully understood what was going on. Also, sometimes Emily could be so lovely....

I began to think that the world was just too pushy, too demanding. Yes, she was different, but did that make her wrong? Who has the right to draw the line between acceptable and non-acceptable behaviour? Was this a politically-correct way of telling me that my daughter was thick? Or retarded? Or mentally ill? It seemed to me that I was being forced to decide on Emily's behalf whether to try to make her as 'normal' as other kids, or to let her be herself.

Making that decision had to include some consideration of the family as a whole. The main attraction of the drugs was that they would give us a chance of living like an ordinary family. Jonathan was refusing to accept that anything could be wrong with his special daughter anyway so, for him, and for our relationship, the thought of having a more normal existence was very tempting.

He was never actively involved in all the to-ing and fro-ing with doctors, psychologists and psychiatrists and had the results relayed by me (an emotional me) at weekends.

Jonathan never saw how she was with other people. He was never at the end of the telephone when school called with a problem, or when angry parents called to relate an issue between Emily and their child. He never stood at the school gate and heard the whisperings of other parents, and he never braved the supermarket dealing with Emily in a tyrannical mood.

Tom was also having a tough time. Her tantrums and unpredictable behaviour were taking their toll on his confidence and security and when she was in wild mode he would come and climb onto my lap. He was spending too much time on my left hip, just as he had done as a baby, while I tried to do other things. I never seemed to spend enough time playing with him on his own. Emily in a temper was frightening for me, an adult, so goodness only knows what it felt like for him to witness as a five year old. She took so much of my attention that I was often exhausted and he missed out on quality time with me. He took to sleeping in my bed and, even though I would carefully return him to his own bed in the middle of the night, he would be there beside me again in the morning.

Finally, I went back to the neurologist at the Children's Hospital in Washington. I had liked him and felt I could trust him. I asked him what it felt like to have ADHD – what was it like for Emily? There had been so much debate about how she should fit into school and society, but that has to do with how the rest of the world relates to her. What about how she can relate to the world? He told me that for Emily the world is like a circus in her head and she cannot ignore the jugglers to concentrate on the elephants. Everything in the world has equal noise. A man mowing the lawn outside the window makes as much demand on her attention as a teacher at the blackboard.

The neurologist explained that because Emily was acting in an 'outrageous' way, other people backed away from her, giving her a bad experience of herself which could cause long-term damage to her self-esteem and her sense of self. The drugs recommended by the psychiatrist would allow her to relax and be herself, rather than continuing to live in overdrive. Her life is simply exhausting because she is so over-stimulated by everything around her. As her mother I needed to consider how to improve her quality of life.

Well, that did it. How could I not put her on the drugs?

After three months of medication, during which time we had close contact with a psychiatrist who adjusted the dosage and monitored Emily's progress, I began to realise that we were living with a different person. We were given heaps of advice on behaviour modification, which I followed to the letter, and then a personal tutor, a wonderful woman with fly-away hair and laughing eyes, was engaged to help Emily learn to learn.

My little girl, now seven and a half, learned to read, write, spell, express herself verbally, deal with tantrums, play with other kids, and engage with other people – all in three months. It was as if the medication turned on a light and the world became clear for her. For the first time in her life Emily was able to control herself and be part of the world around her. She could focus on things. Life became less chaotic for all of us and Emily herself was so much happier. She began to make friends, became well known for rather creative and charming presentations of her work at school and was chosen for a scholarship at the Corcoran School of Art for a series of Saturday workshops. I was so proud of her.

I took her to the psychiatrist once a week to begin with, then once a month. She made such enormous progress that there were even times when I dared to think that we had cracked it. But my background reading had alerted me to the process of change, growth and development in ADHD children, so I continued to keep a watchful eye.

We finally began to make the most of our time in Washington. We had a great group of friends and some wonderful neighbours.

As a family we did a lot of travelling around the States, exploring Arizona, New Mexico, Utah and, closer to home, we had

Chesapeake Bay for weekend trips, Virginia and Maryland. As Jonathan was only home for weekends we made these very special times. The beautiful Rock Creek National Park was on our doorstep and we all fell in love with skiing. We joined the YMCA in Maryland where we played tennis and swam and the children took part in summer camp activities. There were the annual school picnics; July 4th (Independence Day) celebrations and Thanksgivings – we were even snowed in for ten days one winter. We had racoons in our dustbins and kidnapped a neighbour's dog on a regular basis for walks up to Fort Reno.

Many friends and family came to visit from England and I really enjoyed playing 'hotel' for them all. I also have a number of family members in the States and it was great to see more of them. With my close friends, Janette and Bob and their family, in LA we were able to do many trips and holidays with them, in particular, a trip up the California coast and skiing in the Rockies.

We managed to continue living life to the full in spite of the problems with Emily. Quite honestly, I believed that we were back on an even keel. Life felt very good indeed.

# Chapter 3

★ ☆ ★

I still knew that I was a long way from becoming the mother I had always hoped I would be. I used to watch other mothers carefully, noting how they related to their children, and found myself wanting. However, I did discover heaps of patience that I never knew I possessed and when I felt too angry and frustrated I went to the gym, or swam, or did an aerobics class. Yet I never believed that my own resources allowed me to cope well enough. I felt as if I were living life on eggshells.

I also had the conviction that nobody likes a loser, and this caused me to put a lot of energy into presenting the image of a happy, confident and together person to the outside world. I joined a book club, saw friends (and made light to them of how I felt) planned special parties for the children, organised lots of play-dates for them, joined the school PTA and worked on marketing for their fundraising events. I also took a part time job as a marketing consultant for the charity, NOFAS (National Organisation on Foetal Alcohol Syndrome). Looking back I am embarrassed to admit that I buried myself in anything and everything in order to persuade myself that life was normal. I hid my feelings so successfully that even I came to believe that all was well, I was in control and I was happy.

But in the dark hours, of which there were many as I was effectively alone every evening, the 'Why me?' issues began to shape themselves into spectres. A powerful sense of guilt spread itself like a stain across my soul. In some way I felt responsible for Emily's ADHD, as if this was payback time for the many things I had done in my life that I had regretted. I was not a good enough person to be a mother. I didn't have the skills to be a natural mother. But a mother I was, and there was no going back.

The more I tried to look inside myself the less I liked what I found there. It was all too easy to blame myself for Emily not being 'quite right'. Was it because I went back to work and left her? Certainly there had been times when I had been happy to escape her demands. Perhaps I did not love her enough?

At this time my reading and research took me into the 'nature versus nurture' debate. Some professionals were adamant that ADHD was caused by environmental factors such as food/colourings, lack of essential vitamins and minerals, and pollutants, as well as psychosocial elements like attachment (the mother/child bond), self-esteem and so on. Others were convinced that the condition is genetic.

It was not too difficult to look back into my family history and find a large number of eccentric and unusual people, egocentric and creative, exciting but difficult. I also have a brother, 12 years my junior, who was thought to be autistic. So that was it then, it was my fault (as I knew it must be) it was because of my genes!

The genes I could do nothing about, but there were other things I could try to change. I read lots of information about food, additives and supplements and started to change the family's eating habits. I already knew about the obvious things – sugar and fizzy drinks had an instant impact on the children, making them scratchy and hyperactive. I had always cooked proper food for them; we ate very little fast or convenience foods, and I tried out supplements such as zinc and cod liver oil.

I became almost obsessive about all the latest behaviour modification techniques – 1 2 3 Magic, star charts, you name it, I tried it! Understandably, the children began to roll their eyes when I began to explain the next new scheme. Some of it seemed to work, but never for very long and I became disillusioned with it all in the end. I never completely gave up on trying out new ideas but my expectations of success in managing to effect real changes were significantly reduced.

When Emily was nine years old I hit an extremely challenging time in my own life, which must have had a huge effect on her. This was provoked by the death of my mother, from whom I had been estranged for some years, although I had always hoped for some sort of reconciliation. It hurt me deeply that, no matter what I did or said, her tone with me was bitter and unforgiving.

She had had an unhappy marriage to my father, which had ended in divorce. It didn't help that I adored him and was like him in many ways.

My older brother and I became close in our twenties, but both of us had a difficult relationship with my younger sister, and none of us had any real relationship with our younger brother who, at that time, was in prison for drug and burglary offences. Not the ideal family background but one I had grown up with, and learned to cope with, in my own way.

Somehow the juxtaposition of these family issues with my own situation — Emily and my ever-absent husband — sent me crashing down into despair. I could not cope with the smallest thing. I would be driving to collect the children from school and have to pull off the road because I was shaking with tears. I was angry and hurt that my mother had chosen to cut me out of her will, something that I have never managed to understand. Before we left to live in the States I had been the one to host many of the family get- togethers, and I had tried to build bridges by taking the children to Oxford to see her, or having her to stay so that she could spend time with them and have the opportunity to develop close relationships with them. These were her only grandchildren — why did she never seem to love them, or me? I would never know.

I had kept a lid on self-pity for a long time but now it threatened to swamp me. I ended up on Prozac, a popular anti-depressant in the States at that time. It helped me to get myself back in line but it did not address any of the real issues which had caused the depression. Instead it boosted my already super-efficient ability to bury my own problems, put on a happy face and just carry on.

In April my husband's company was involved in a takeover and we were recalled to England at very short notice. Suddenly our life in Washington came to an end and I found myself thrown into house-hunting back in England, searching for schools, packing and shipping, and tying up the loose ends of my life in the States - all in three months.

The move home was awkward. Tom did not remember living in England, so as far as he was concerned, he was moving abroad. Emily, now so happy and settled, was being uprooted from our safe and accepting community. I felt as if I had been cut adrift from the support network that I had built in Washington. Still, the prospect of 'going home' had always been there; it had just come sooner than expected.

My feet did not touch the ground and I felt invigorated by the move back. No time to think, and every day filled with moving, packing, farewell parties, a trip to Hilton Head, South Carolina, to fill the gap between leaving our Washington home and moving into our new home in England. It was all very exciting. We bought a very run-down house near Wimbledon, planning to completely refurbish it over the next couple of years, and arranged for the children to start new schools in September.

Arriving back in England during the summer holidays was both fun and fraught. It was great to catch up with people who I had not seen since we had been overseas and being back close to family was immensely rewarding. Unpacking boxes into a dingy and rather forlorn house in a strange neighbourhood was less rewarding − our new neighbours all seemed to be enclosed behind tall hedges and electronic gates and were therefore hard to make contact with.

The first big shock came when the schools that we had thought looked so promising for the children (just a short walk from our new home) did not offer places to either of them and we had to investigate all the alternatives quickly before the schools closed for the summer break. Eventually we came across a great private school for Emily in Wimbledon but still had no place for Tom. By the end of the summer the local primary school had allocated him a place but it was all rather stressful.

Also stressful was the fact that our new GP refused to continue to prescribe Emily's medication in spite of all our carefully-prepared reports on her condition, notes from our paediatrician in the States and a letter from her psychiatrist. I could not believe it. I just hit a brick wall with the National Health Service. They simply would not understand what we had been through in the States and were refusing to help. Eventually we were forced to find a solution in the private sector, which cost us the earth. A private psychiatrist and private prescriptions have been a constant drain on our finances over the years.

Tom was finding it very difficult to settle and was becoming increasingly volatile. He seemed to be constantly exploding with rage and was becoming very destructive. One day he destroyed the garden house in a temper, smashing the glass doors, luckily without hurting himself. I put this down to the disruption of moving and tried to give him lots of attention but I was left with a nagging doubt that all was not well, and that it was not going to simply go away.

One day in late September I collapsed in the hallway of our new home and ended up in hospital, where I had my appendix and an ovarian cyst removed. I found it very hard to recover from all the drama of this event and spent the next few months gradually falling into an abyss of exhaustion. Finally I was diagnosed with Chronic Fatigue Syndrome.

Living with CFS is terribly difficult with two young children but, yet again, I developed a way of managing things. I would take them to school, then come home and go straight to bed, making certain that I had set the alarm in time to go to collect them again. I also started to see a therapist, which I found a real lifeline – she kept me sane during this time. Through our conversations I began to understand how inadequate some of my coping strategies had been over the years and what I needed to do to be better able to deal with Emily's, and increasingly Tom's, difficult behaviour. I gave in to the need to rest and learned to accept that I would always be less than perfect, but that that was OK. This became my own 'time out' and I used it to start to rethink my life.

Accepting that I was a 'good enough' person, as a mother and as a wife was an important turning point for me but it was not until a few years later that I realised the significance of this concept. Once I recovered from CFS I became determined to put everything right. My marriage had suffered terribly because I had been unable to cope with the relationship as well as the difficulties with the children and my tiredness.

By the age of seven Tom too was diagnosed with ADHD. This was a devastating blow. Once again I was plunged back into the 'why me?' syndrome and for a while I found it very difficult to accept the diagnosis and asked for a second, and then a third, opinion before I could believe it. He was such a different child to Emily and for a long time I had thought that he was simply mirroring her behaviour. But the test results, together with his behaviour at school and at home, left little room for doubt.

The combination of Emily and Tom was a recipe for disaster. They would simply wind each other up until one of them lost control. Things got broken, someone got hurt and I played 'piggy in the middle'. Once again family life had disintegrated and, despite some calm moments, it was often like living in a battlefield. Tom also went on medication and both children attended the same psychiatrist who, once he understood the family dynamics, tried to be supportive. But our visits to him were infrequent, and again I found myself dealing with the day-to-day situation on my own.

Around this time both children again changed schools. Emily, at the age of eleven, had outgrown her Preparatory School and got a place at Surbiton High School. Tom, now eight, went to a local boys' Preparatory School. They continued on their medication and life, if never on an even keel exactly, was manageable. I made it my business to engage with both schools, providing information and support to teachers on how to manage ADHD children, hoping that this would help them to care for and educate my children.

At this time I discovered an organisation called the Hyperactive Children's Support Group and began to get involved in its activities. I met a wonderful neighbour, Marion, who has become a real support and together we are now Trustees of the charity. Through this group I am kept well-informed about new research and developments in the field and finally got to meet other parents who have children like mine.

There were many good times and I felt optimistic that, with careful management, both children could lead normal lives. Emily settled in well at her new school and started to show real promise in art and music. She also joined the ski club and was soon an active member of the school team, travelling around the country, and even to France to compete. She made a number of good friends, all of whom were extremely tolerant of her rather volatile behaviour. Forever on the edge, and pushing all the boundaries, she still continued to do very well academically. She had always been a beautiful child but now became quite stunningly attractive. Ever the centre of attention, she seemed to be the life and soul of any situation, drawing others to her.

Our family expanded to include a black Labrador puppy whom we called Harry. He quickly became an important part of our family and turned out to be the most soppy, gentle, loving character you would ever wish to meet. He became my little shadow around the house – and was also the only 'child' in our home who would do as I asked!

But then the rug slipped from beneath our feet when Jonathan was made redundant. For the first time ever he was very much in and around the home, and it was a whole year before he found another job. I had been intending to begin retraining as a psychologist but my plans had to be put on hold while we reappraised our life.

During the twelve months that followed we looked at many possible life changes but, in the end, Jonathan opted for a position in a major corporation, based in Manchester. Jobs were far from easy to come by at this time and casualties from redundancies were running high. We agreed that it would be a temporary fix, so there would be no sense in moving house at this point. With the future looking a little more certain I decided to make sure that I did something for myself while Jonathan lived away from home. I applied to do a Masters (MSc) in Counselling Psychology at Surrey University, and was accepted onto the programme.

On Jonathan's first day in his new job we got a call from Tom's school advising that he was being asked to leave following a spate of bad behaviour. Yes, his behaviour had never been exactly good, but this decision was not in any way reasonable. Discussions followed, but their minds were made up – they no longer wanted him at the school and therefore there was no point in fighting about it. It was not until his final day there that I discovered they had not been giving him his medication at school and thus, by the afternoons, he was frequently out of control. I was livid, but powerless to do anything.

It was difficult to try to explain to Tom that he could no longer go to his school. His whole life at this time revolved around his school friends and his sport. Much of my social life was also bound up with the parents of his friends, standing on the touch line at rugby matches, social events at school and dinner parties at weekends. Suddenly he and I felt cast out of a community, which had been so comfortable and enjoyable.

Once again I felt the pain of being judged by others to be not quite good enough, my son not worthy to be a part of that team. I became embarrassed to bump into parents from the school and expected, as happened before when Emily was asked to leave her school in Washington, to be dropped by these people who had become such an important part of our lives.

In reality, that did not happen and a handful of people we knew, and their sons, have remained important friends. Nonetheless, that community now seemed closed to us. I even began to hate the headmaster, to the point where thinking of him could produce a violent anger within me – how dare he pass such a judgement on a 10-year-old boy? But in the end these feelings were only destructive and I had to force myself to put the sorry episode behind me, and try to move on.

Writing this now I still feel the loss for us both, and there are many moments when Tom is home for the holidays that I regret he is no longer part of that group. I feel angry that a school can decide to oust a student who does not conform to their ideal and who threatens to lower their status in the national school league tables. It seems that some schools now exist for the promotion of the head teacher, rather than for the students, and anyone who does not fit the correct image must go elsewhere. I come across this time and time again talking to other parents of 'different' children and it sickens me.

# Chapter 4

With Jonathan in Manchester all week, my father helped me to search for a new school for Tom. None of the local day schools would take him and we were forced into looking at boarding schools. Finally we found Eagle House, where he could be a weekly boarder. This was never what I had imagined for Tom. I had never thought of him going away to school at all, least of all at the age of 10, but it turned out to be a really good choice for him. He was happy and thrived there. With hindsight, and given what was about to happen with Emily, I am forever grateful that he was not living at home.

During the Easter holidays, we took a family holiday to Cuba, which turned out to be a mistake. We had had a lean year, with Jonathan being out of work, and this trip was something of a celebration. Family holidays can always be tricky, but for ours somehow all the problems and wrinkles play themselves out and are magnified by our expectations of 'having a good time'. It is a tall order to balance Jonathan's need for rest and recuperation, my need for adventure in a new place and the children's demands. Invariably in turns into a running battle, trying to contain the children's hyperactivity and lack of awareness of the impact they may have on others around them, while sustaining the illusion that we are spending 'quality' time together. Holidays like this never did any of us any good, and created more problems than they solved.

Now nearly 13, Emily was beginning to assert her authority and control over everyone and everything. She was becoming quite aggressive in her tactics and was learning how to drive a wedge between Jonathan and myself, playing one of us off against the other and enjoying the resulting mayhem. I write this as if it was deliberate on her part, I don't really think it was, but it often felt like it. She and Tom clashed, as always, and trying to keep the surface calm became an impossible task.

It had always been a burden that Jonathan had never seemed able to share the effort involved in dealing with the children. I began to harbour a deep resentment that he expected me to deal with all this stuff and be the perfect wife and mother at the same time. It did not help that I had such high personal expectations of myself, equally it did not feel as if I had much choice. We had spent a great deal of our married life apart and were beginning yet another, this time indefinite, period where we would be living at opposite ends of the country. I finally blew a fuse one evening when he confessed that he had taken the position in Manchester because he could not cope with the chaos at home and hold down a reasonable job.

This confirmed all my worst suspicions. He was able to run away from the situation while I woke up to it every morning and dealt with it 24/7. I was furious and told him to go to hell.

Emily continued to flex her muscles. She seemed to be deliberately defying our requirements for reasonable behaviour and was becoming abusive and challenging our authority as parents. Some of this, I am sure, was the beginning of hormonal and teenage issues, but I asked myself, for the thousandth time: 'How much of this is normal, how much is due to her ADHD? What can we reasonably expect of her? How the hell do I help her to contain herself so that she doesn't cause herself harm?'

I tried to reason with her but began to notice that she was no longer listening. With a small child it is much easier to contain such behaviour and I had developed strategies, like removing her from the situation until she calmed down or agreed to be reasonable. One by one these strategies began to fail. She was physically bigger and it was no longer possible to hold her, in order to calm her. She would fight to put distance between us. Sending her to her room for 'time out' was no longer effective. She would simply refuse to go, or would throw things around in her room, while I was left sitting on the kitchen floor below waiting for her anger to subside.

Increasingly I noticed an apparent lack of connection between her and other people – this was not just a mother/daughter battle. If friends did not do as she wished she became abusive and threatening. Many of her former friends started to drift away and she began to look for people she could dominate.

I tried my best to keep the lines of communication open but frequently found that she was just switching off from me. I felt I was losing touch with my beautiful daughter and she was becoming a tyrant.

One special thing about my children, which is relevant here, is how truly charming they can both be when it suits them. It may seem an odd moment to mention this, but it helps keep a perspective on how they appear to other people. Both are blessed with good looks, tall, lean bodies and deep penetrating eyes; they have real charisma, which is almost magnetic. They have a strong presence in any situation and thus a powerful impact on those around them, and on the atmosphere. Emily is particularly potent. She seems to emanate an energy and electricity, which is impossible to ignore. In this way she exerts a pressure on everyone around her. I think she was born with this electricity.

At the very beginning, when I took Emily to the Lab School in Washington for psychological testing I remember standing in the waiting room and, looking up at the vaulted roof, I realised that the walls were covered with the names of famous people throughout history who were said to have had ADHD or some related learning difficulty. Of course some had been diagnosed retrospectively, but nevertheless the significance of all these names gave me a conviction that my daughter must have some special gift. She must choose whether she offers this gift for the benefit of the world, as Churchill, Einstein, Leonardo da Vinci, Walt Disney, Robin Williams, Whoopi Goldberg, Billy Connolly and so many others have done in many different fields. My role must be to help her grow with strength and confidence and to prompt her to discover her gift.

This may all sound a bit far-fetched, but it is quite important, especially at this point in our story. People who are impossible to live with, and become socially unacceptable, can often do amazing things. I do not suggest that my children will become famous, or do anything of particular note. All I am saying is that 'sideways' people (including my children) often have different paths to tread in their lives.

The reason that I mention this is that when your life starts to come apart one thing you do as a parent is cling on to the hope that somehow this nightmare will have a purpose. You have to give it all you have got and then that purpose will reveal itself. Never deeply religious, I had nonetheless been brought up a Catholic and, cynical as I became about organised religion, I never doubted my deep sense of faith in God.

I really believe this – if I had not I would have fallen into a crumpled heap way before I did. This ideal gave me the energy and the hope that we could get through this awful time.

One of the milestones on our slide into the abyss was the battle of the mobile phone. Emily had been pestering for one for ages and when Jonathan moved to Manchester it seemed the best way to give her immediate access to him. In the first month there were very few calls to Manchester, just a bill for £250! The inevitable warnings and confiscations achieved nothing. The mobile phone became some sort of compulsion for her and a weapon between us. She could not stop tapping out numbers; it was attached to her ear like an earring and any attempt to detach it was met with fury and aggression. Of course, after the phone bill she lost the phone and we put in place a plan for her to earn it back.

One of the problems we have as Emily's parents is our lack of effective sanctions for her bad behaviour. Nothing seemed to matter to her, except the phone, and this became a sanction I used to the full. The problem was that my husband did not agree with this, as he felt she needed to be able to call him. Also, at nearly 13 years old, she was out and about more on her own and needed to be safe. So the phone became a three-way battle, which I consistently lost.

Although Emily never seemed to have any degree of commitment to her work, she had, up to now, been a reasonable student in a fairly demanding school. She is clearly highly intelligent and I believed that, with little effort, she could stay on track well enough. However, her performance at school was deteriorating rapidly, as was her behaviour, and her place there began to feel uncertain. I kept up a regular dialogue with her teachers and Head of Year and we tried many different tactics to try to help her engage in her schoolwork. She was constantly on work cards to discipline her attendance at lessons and was given lots of extra support and leeway on homework assignments. The school was amazingly supportive, but her behaviour in class became increasingly disruptive to the other girls, and there were numerous complaints from other parents.

Jonathan and I had always been keen to encourage our children to try out all kinds of interests and I was always prepared to facilitate these activities, both in and out of school. Emily had shown great promise at ballet when she was younger – she still is a wonderful dancer – but once she got to a level where any serious commitment was required, she gave up. So it was with her flute and piano. There was never any pressure from us for her to do these things but, when she showed promise, there was always lots of encouragement, support and respect. There was little enough to praise her for, so these talents became an important way of showing our pride in her achievements. Sadly, as she withdrew from her schoolwork, she also started to sabotage her accomplishments. She began to lie and deceive us and her teachers about attending lessons, orchestra practice,

practice at home and so on. Her teachers slowly lost heart and she gradually gave it all up.

The only thing that did not slip away for a long time was her skiing. Having learned to ski in the States at a very young age, Emily had a head-start on most of her peers, as well as a lot of basic talent. Even without much concentration she seemed to make the school teams effortlessly (much to the chagrin of her contemporaries). I spent many hours on motorways getting her to training sessions and competitions and came to regard this as a way of us doing something together.

In the past I had frequently involved myself in her activities as a way of supporting her and sharing with her, but this was an area I decided to leave to her. She had to earn her own skis, boots and equipment by showing her commitment to the sport and through her performance. I was tired of simply shelling out money; she was now old enough to understand that she needed to work at things if she was to continue to get our support. So she did, and for a long time this was something that she and I were able to share.

During the summer holidays we always went to the Isle of Wight where we had a regular rental on part of a house on the beach at Seaview. Quite a few of our friends did the same and there was always a good crowd there and plenty going on. We also had friends to stay and my brother Peter, and his wife Liz, would also spend a weekend or so with us. This became a special time for me as it was a place where I could let the children go off to the village on their own and we could walk and talk together for miles along the beach with our dog, Harry. I either cooked all our favourite foods at home or we would spend evenings eating seafood at the Seaview Hotel or the Baywatch café.

Jonathan never really enjoyed these family holidays, but would come down at weekends out of a sense of duty. I think he also truly believed that if he was there everything would be alright. The children loved it and were always desperate to go back the next year. They both had friends, some of whom were there all summer, and there was a tennis court nearby where we could play together. It suited us very well.

But the summer after Emily turned 13 our trip to Seaview was a lot less successful than usual. Jonathan had decided to make it our family holiday for the year as neither of us was inclined to risk repeating the Cuba experience. The problem was that our weekends at home were becoming increasingly fraught, not only with Emily issues, although things often began there, but between the two of us. I was often stressed out and Jonathan would come home exhausted from his week, expecting to find a welcoming family at home. The tension between us would reach breaking point and he would slam out of the house and be 'Mr Grumpy' for the rest of the weekend. I was getting tired and impatient with this, in the same way as I was becoming resentful of him for leaving me to deal with all the 'crap' while he escaped to the peace and solitude of our wonderful designer apartment in Manchester.

Even though I knew it was childish, I had a deep nagging sensation that, while I was busy tending (unsuccessfully) to the needs of everyone else in the family, no one was attending to mine. I was certain that my share of the family load was unreasonable and that I was not able to cope with it. Yet I knew Jonathan couldn't deal with it either, so I felt trapped. I also resented Jonathan's well-meaning attempts to play 'piggy in the middle' between Emily and myself. He often played judge without full knowledge of the details and, as a result, any authority I had over Emily was undermined. I was becoming increasingly upset and angry. I felt like a volcano about to erupt.

The breaking point came over something rather trivial. I packed the car for our trip to Seaview. Jonathan, who had come back from Manchester late the night before, was slow to pack and was as morose as ever. I was tight-lipped and the children were uncooperative. We had a ferry to catch.

Jonathan did not feel that there was enough room left in the car – packed tight as it was with bedding, dog, and everything but the kitchen sink – so he announced that he was not coming on holiday. At any other time I would have done my usual smoothing of ruffled feathers but this time I did not. I drove off to the ferry without him.

I cursed and cried and shouted all the way down the A3 to Portsmouth. The children and the dog sat in silence. I raged and raged.

'That's it!' I yelled to no one in particular, 'That is the end of my marriage!'

The children rarely saw me lose control and I suspect that they were in a state of shock. I managed to calm down while waiting to board the ferry, but my mind was made up. I called our answerphone at home telling Jonathan to go to hell, then switched my phone off so there could be no further discussion.

We crossed the Solent to the island and my mood was still volatile. The children were quiet and cautious. When we got to the house I set about the unpacking with a vengeance. The children went off with the dog and I sat with a glass of wine gazing out at the sea and reviewing the events of the day.

I realised that I desperately needed some space. I woke each day to the storms of Emily (or else a deathly silence – almost as bad) and our evenings were regular battles over homework, computer (MSN messaging) and phone. I just never felt I could relax with her. It was almost as if she was sapping all my emotional energy, leaving me to collapse into bed completely drained. I couldn't go on like this; but how else was I to go on? Perhaps if I tried to manage the children on my own it would be easier. I was beginning to feel as sapped by Jonathan's needs as by Emily's. Between them I always felt like the bad guy – the only one who said 'No' all the time.

Also, why did I feel I had to deal with Jonathan's anger all the time? He was fighting his own battles at work and was frequently raging at the world; the incompetence of his colleagues, other drivers on the road, Emily's behaviour and so on. Everything in our lives had become so negative - it was like moving through treacle, only it was not sweet. When did I last really have a laugh? My girlfriends seemed to have become the only bit of my life that I enjoyed. Thank God for them.

Later that night Jonathan turned up on the doorstep. Apparently the children had phoned him from the village and asked him to come. We walked for miles in the dark along the beach talking and in the end I softened. I meant what I had said, but I did not know what else to do, so I agreed not to end our marriage.

When we got back to the house the children had cooked a pasta supper and made a romantic setting in the dining room with candles. They had put themselves to bed, but we were aware of a scuffling on the landing above as we sat down at the table. This was the first time they had done anything like this. I cried and cried. Whatever happened I was convinced we must stick together as a family.

After a week Jonathan returned to Manchester as planned and, that terrible day apparently forgotten, life went back to normal. But I did not. Something had shifted inside me and I felt extremely fragile.

# Chapter 5

The battle of the mobile phone was gathering momentum, Emily was stealing money from me in increasingly worrying amounts and, because she was denying it all, I was setting traps to catch her. She was becoming a very angry person, defiant and seriously oppositional. Seeking her cooperation over the smallest thing had become tiring and aggravating. Continuing in my usual role of peacemaker, I felt as though I were walking on eggshells to get through the day with the least amount of drama.

It was during this summer that Emily started to just go off on her own, defying our iron rule that we must know where she is at all times, approve where she is going and agree a return time. She constantly violated all these basic rules of safety and trust and fought bitterly over any sanctions. Much of her anger was directed at me because I was the one in charge of discipline and that summer I became known to her friends as 'The Bitch'.

A girlfriend, Debbie, and her children came to stay for our second week in Seaview. I was very fond of my circle of girlfriends but, before now, had been reluctant to share with them the true extent of my feelings. I had the idea that even people who seem eager to share stuff are unwilling to accept your burdens. This outspoken and very caring friend proved me wrong. We talked and talked until I ran out of words. It became clear that I had not been as good as I imagined about concealing my troubles and I was relieved to be pouring them out without holding back.

My need for space and time to myself was now urgent and Debbie pressed me into going off for the day on my own while she did things with the children. I spent the time in Bembridge, sitting on the beach in the sand, in the freezing cold, and did some careful thinking. There was no doubt that our life as a family was falling apart. I felt as if I were a circus entertainer spinning plates in the air on the end of sticks, rushing from plate to plate to keep them from crashing to the ground. I had become an unwilling performer. I was exhausted and the plates were about to fall and break.

I struggled on but was in bad shape. For once I couldn't seem to pull myself together. I decided to limp down to my father's house on the way back from Seaview for some tender loving care. He lives in the heart of Gloucestershire in a wonderful old Cotswold stone house with my stepmother, Sue (GrandSue to the children). I have always felt incredibly close to them both and love spending time with these two very special people. They have always tried to be there for me and I have always been able to open up to them.

Visiting Dad and Sue involves lots of energy-restoring activities like trekking amongst the beautiful Cotswold hills which come right down to their doorstep, eating supper by candlelight in the thatched summer house, and lots of attention. I poured out all my troubles and, in recounting them, managed to see a way forward. Leaving the children and Harry with them, I drove up to Manchester with a mission.

I arrived at Jonathan's flat, which I was seeing for the first time since we had bought it six months before. Looking around I could see what a stunning home he had made – all glass and chrome, very minimalist, with designer furniture and our oil paintings from Cuba. The effect was not only extremely tasteful but also serene, without the clobber and mess of children and the dog. A sanctuary.

The main problem we were facing was that Emily was successfully driving a wedge between us, playing each of us off against the other, and dominating family life to the extent that she consumed us both. As a result we had no time or energy left for our relationship and, in our mutual resentment of the situation, were blaming each other.

I suggested to Jonathan that I wanted to take some time apart so that we would stop destroying our relationship and, during that time, would put every effort into straightening out Emily. It would give me the chance to try to deal with the problems one by one, rather than trying to untangle the whole complicated mess. Without Emily interfering between us we would be able to repair our feelings for each other. Jonathan's job has always been a fairly all-consuming thing for him and home was not giving him the rest and calm that he needed in order to cope with his own stress. He could use this space to sort himself out and get his job up and running.

Jonathan took this as total rejection. It threatened his view of his role within the family and he didn't seem to quite believe that I wasn't telling him our marriage was over. The next couple of days were a nightmare. Neither of us slept. He started to visibly fall apart with anguish and I found myself torn between being responsible for all this mess and wanting to run away. I thought I would leave in the middle of the night, it was the only way I could possible remain firm in my plan. But how could I leave him in pieces like this? I couldn't quite do it. I felt so needed, that if I left he would disintegrate.

In September Tom started at his new boarding school and, although he settled in quite quickly, I missed him terribly. In October I began my postgraduate course in Counselling Psychology at the University of Surrey. Studying for this qualification had become an important way of getting a life of my own and I was determined that it would eventually lead to a career as a counsellor, helping other families with difficult children. It was my way of bringing together a number of threads in my life and making them add up to something positive and worthwhile. A way of justifying the struggles and making use of the lessons learned.

From the start I loved being absorbed into the academic atmosphere, meeting an entirely new set of people, from all walks of life, with whom I shared a common goal. I had not written an essay since my undergraduate days and had trouble initially clearing the cobwebs from my brain, but it was stimulating, absorbing and challenging and it also took me out of the home and away from the problems there.

I was also involved with my father's business at this time. He and Sue run a management training and consulting business and I was able to use all my marketing skills to support them as they moved into different areas. It was also work that I could wrap around the demands of the family.

I worked with my father on a project implementing his ideas in a Charter School in California and later carried out a research project involving some of his franchisees in America, Canada, South Africa, Finland, Norway and England to assess the viability of putting his 'Thinking Intentions Profile' on-line. Having grown up with this work in its developmental stages it was very rewarding to be playing a part in it now. I felt honoured to be working with him and his colleagues.

As a result of all this my life became very busy and I began to feel more in control and more purposeful. Instead of facing my inadequacies as a mother I was out in the world doing things that I enjoyed and that made me feel I was making something of my life at last.

For anyone standing on the outside and looking in we must have given the appearance of a perfectly normal family, even though Emily and I were on our own during the week, with Tom and Jonathan home at the weekend. Jonathan and I led a busy social life seeing friends, going to the theatre, giving dinner parties – the same as everyone else we knew. Tom was well settled into his school and I got used to Jonathan living away. Emily was wonderful in a ballet show at Christmas and we spent New Year skiing.

Emily was, by this time, doing all the teenage stuff with a vengeance. I tried as far as possible to meet her demands for independence but it was tough going. The battles between us now included her total refusal to do any schoolwork and her obsession with boys and music. Her lies and deceit about where she was, and with whom, became legendary and I knew I was losing all my trust in her to do the right thing. She was increasingly rude and abusive and was drawing steadily away from me.

Weekends were as tense as ever as Emily continued to pit Jonathan and myself against each other and would end all too often with Jonathan slamming out of the house having had enough. It was getting to a stage where he was constantly angry and morose and I found myself just getting through these times together by switching off. I would do the laundry and make a family Sunday roast and just wait for him to go back to Manchester leaving me to pick up the pieces with Emily during the week.

School was becoming less patient with Emily's behaviour, and had concerns about her academic performance, but no matter what I said or did I could not get Emily to take anything seriously. I was powerless enough at home, so I had no hope of influencing her at school. She had earned a reputation, with teachers and other girls, as wild and out of control. She was always in trouble, always the bad guy. Other parents were beginning to blame her for their own daughters getting up to mischief and there were a lot of missed lessons, and failures to come home off the school bus.

When Emily qualified to represent the school at the National Schools Ski Championships in Chamonix, in France, the headmistress initially refused to grant her leave of absence from school, but eventually we agreed that this might be the thing to help with her self-esteem and bring her back into the fold at school. Her friend Alex had also qualified and, as they were both too young to go unaccompanied, Alex's family were travelling with them. At the last moment my brother, Peter, decided to come with Emily and me.

Our accommodation was so poky that Peter had to stay at a local hotel, but Emily and I were next door to the ski school where she was to train every day for the races at the end of the week. During the day Peter and I skied with Alex's family and we spent the evenings in the local cafes or at the ski school.

From the start of the trip Emily was terribly antagonistic. She hated me being there and would hardly acknowledge my presence, let alone talk to me or allow me to share in her experiences. She also took every opportunity to escape from me. I found her habit of going missing extremely hard to cope with as I had become worried about her being so wild and irresponsible – I was genuinely afraid for her. She did not seem to care what she did or said, boys found her far too exciting and, frankly, I was often totally embarrassed by her behaviour and what others were saying about her. The homework set by the school was abandoned. I knew I would have a problem when we got back to school but I could do nothing about it.

Nevertheless, I was proud that she had got so far with her skiing and I really wanted her to do her best. I kept any confrontation to a minimum and tried to get through the week. Jo, Alex's mum, and I are great friends and I was extremely grateful that I didn't have to deal with all this on my own. She was a great support to me that week, and has been ever since.

Race day arrived and we all went up the mountain to watch. It was a beautiful day, freezing cold but with bright blue skies. As it was a major event everyone was taking it very seriously. Emily was totally hyper but I just thought it was amazing that she was even taking part. My brother was up and down the slope taking photographs, while Jo and I waited at the finishing post.

Watching her set off out of the starting gate I could not believe it was really her. This girl who had so often refused to even put her skis on. I had often suffered at the top of a mountain trying to deal with her tantrums, refusing to go a step further – you could never lead her or follow her down. Now here she was looking like a professional racer in her skin-tight racing suit and chrome helmet and going like a bat out of hell.

As she flung herself over the finishing line I realised that the commentator was announcing that her time was the third best so far and I rushed towards her in excitement. She, however, had a different agenda. Without even looking at me she turned to her new friends for celebratory hugs and shrieks of delight. To hide my embarrassment I took myself off towards a pack of husky dogs, the tears freezing on my cheeks. As soon as I could get myself in check, I returned to the celebrations and acted as if nothing had happened.

Peter had to return home before the medals ceremony on the Saturday, but I went along with Jo and we stood in the snow waiting for the prizes to be presented. Both girls had done fantastically well and had each ended up with Bronze medals. It was more than I had ever hoped for, yet the week had been a terrible strain and I felt totally depressed. I waited for Emily's name to be announced, camera poised in my hand, watching as others walked up to the stage to collect their prizes and have their photos taken by their proud parents. It was a festive occasion and many of us in the crowd had got to know each other well during the week. There was to be a party afterwards and people were in high spirits.

Emily's turn came and I pressed forward in the crowd with my camera, but as I did so she deliberately turned her back on me to make it impossible to capture the moment.

Everyone looked at me, wondering what was going on. I was mortified, totally humiliated. Without really thinking I just turned and fled through the crowd, back to our poky little room. I cried and cried and couldn't stop. I felt so deeply wounded. How could she do that? Why?

Jo came to the rescue but I just couldn't face anyone. Eventually I pulled myself together, joined them for dinner and drank far too much wine. I didn't bother looking for Emily, who presumably stayed at the ski school and partied. I eventually caught up with her late that night but she wasn't speaking to me, and I wasn't speaking to her either.

# Chapter 6

★ ✩ ★

In April I started to see my first clients as a trainee counsellor at a local GP Practice and really began to get a taste of what it would feel like to be a real counsellor. All my work was carefully supervised and, as part of my course requirement, I began to see a therapist on a weekly basis. The course was going really well and, while Emily was at school, I was involved in my studies, meeting deadlines on assignments and generally trying to get on with my life.

But the evenings were much less within my control. Emily was either aggressive and abusive, or retreated into herself. With her friends she was still pushy and loud, but I was beginning to think that she really did not like herself. She was dealing with a lot of criticism from teachers and girls at school, and her best friend had been moved to another school by her parents in order to separate the two girls.

Emily and a few local friends had been hanging out on the site of a partly-built house down the road and one night her friend, Olivia, was quite badly injured as a result of a wall collapsing. The place was out of bounds, of course, but just two nights later they were all arrested there by the police and brought to my house, which was the closest. They were given a severe talking to and were threatened with prosecution for trespassing if they were caught again. They had all been drinking and smoking dope. The boys were 15 and 16 years old but Emily was still only 13 and Olivia, still in stitches and bandages from the last incident at the site, was only 12.

I grounded Emily for a month – she was not allowed out at all and this meant she would miss a party that weekend. On the Saturday night she tried to sneak out of the house and a huge row ensued. Things got a little out of hand and she was sent to her room. Jonathan and I could hear her up there smashing things and crashing around. She was in a total rage and, not for the first time, I was really frightened. Suddenly we heard the smashing of glass. Jonathan raced up the stairs and when he finally got her to open the door her room was totally wrecked and covered with shards of glass from a broken full-length mirror.

After clearing up the glass, Jonathan left her to tidy up. It was a long time before she reappeared and when she did it was immediately apparent that she had cut her wrists. Not badly, thank God, there was no need to rush to hospital, but we were still badly shaken.

I contacted our family doctor and tried to get an appointment with her psychiatrist but there was little else we could do except worry ourselves sick about it. She kept pushing the limits further and further. She seemed to know no bounds.

Not long after this episode I had another occasion to ground her. She was now going off fairly often and I would never know where, or with whom. I would drive myself mad calling all her friends trying to track her down and would get terribly angry when at last she came back. One evening I had been going spare with worry and we had a fearful row. Emily, after being sent to her room, decided to climb out of her window and onto the roof in order to leave home. I heard her on the roof, which was wet and slippery with rain, but could not persuade her to climb back in. She sat out there for three hours in the rain while I sat on the kitchen floor listening for any noise of movement. I slowly worked myself up into a frenzy of anger, helplessness and despair. I was frightened she might fall and I was also terrified what else she might do. In the end I went to my neighbours for help. It was close to midnight by this time and I just couldn't take any more. Joan and her husband, Einar, were wonderful. I sat with Einar while Joan talked Emily into coming back off the roof.

Emily's attempts to leave the house without my consent began to increase, and she would often go to Olivia's house. It was quite a while before I realised that the reason they took her in was, in part, due to the terrible stories she would tell them about her life at home. Many of the stories were just simply untrue, but there were often elements of truth. I was all too often angry or upset with her and her father was becoming much more physical in the anger and distress she was causing him.

I reached a point where I no longer felt able to cope with Emily at home and we agreed that I should look for a boarding school for her. Her school approved, and were helpful with suggestions, and I was soon exploring the options. But Emily decided that this was not what she wanted at all – it would interfere with her social life and she wanted to stay at her current school. I could see that this would soon no longer be possible and therefore continued to try to find the right place for her, but each time I found somewhere that I thought might be suitable she would sabotage her interview and the possibility of a place then became a non-starter.

Then I found St Mary's in Shaftesbury, Dorset, which I really felt would be the best possible school for Emily. I engaged the support of her current school, and the psychiatrist, both of whom wrote their reports. Everything seemed to be progressing well. Emily spent a few days at home, unwilling to go to school, and during that time I really tried to talk to her, but, in the end, I said that this was not her choice to make, that we, as her parents, were doing the very best we could for her. At this point I really felt that she was at last coming round to the idea. But then, two days before she was due to leave, everything fell apart. Emily spoke to her father on the phone and reported back that he had said we would not force her to go if she did not want to. She refused to go.

To say I was angry would be an understatement. I was livid with

Jonathan. I am sure he did not intend the conversation to have this result, but it did, and there was no going back. Luckily, Surbiton High took her back, but for how long? The whole incident showed me just how powerful Emily was now and I was bubbling over with fury at Jonathan for his lack of support.

You might have expected that, having been so close to losing her place at Surbiton High, Emily would at least try to pull herself together at school. But no, in her end of year exams she failed eight out of eleven subjects, not marginally, but by a long way. The school made her re-sit some of the exams before the end of term but the others she would re-take in September. Although she had chosen subjects for her GCSE courses, which she would start next term, she had not met the standard required to even begin them.

Another difficult summer followed. We borrowed a friend's cottage in Cornwall and took a school friend of Emily's with us. Within minutes of arriving in the lovely seaside village of Crackington Haven, Emily and her friend had made contact with a group of local louts and that set the pace for the week. The boys (and there were only boys in the group) just hung around the village, bored and looking for trouble. One of them had a car and another looked permanently stoned (we saw his father in the pub one night and he looked as if he spent his time permanently drunk!). The low point of the week was the day when the two girls went down to the beach before breakfast and we saw no more of them.

When my search reached the café on the beach I was told that they had been seen going off in the car with 'the lads'. They were nowhere to be found and we could not leave the cottage in case they returned. I spent the day wondering at what point we should call the police – it was dreadful. I also felt responsible for Emily's friend. What on earth would I tell her parents?

Seven and a half hours later the girls wandered into the cottage as if they had just popped down to the local shop. Jonathan tore them off a strip for being so irresponsible and that night we had serious discussions about what could have happened and how selfish they had been. Emily was scarcely engaging in the conversation and took herself off to bed in the middle of it.

Our annual trip to Sea view was more of the same – Jonathan and I were both on edge. On our first night, when we were leaving the Sea view hotel where we had been to supper with my brother and his wife, Jonathan totally lost his temper and struck Emily. She had been provocative all evening, causing the usual tense atmosphere and I cannot blame him for being so angry, but I could not condone him hitting her. Although he was full of remorse later, I'm afraid I was less than sympathetic, as he had been moody ever since we had arrived. The next day, while the rest of us were on a walk along the coast to Bembridge, Jonathan left the island without even saying goodbye.

Emily seemed set now on a path of self destruction, taking me with her. I was back on Prozac and Jonathan and I were becoming increasingly distant from each other. Tom began to retreat into his Playstation games when things started to look dodgy. Even the dog began to seek shelter in his basket once voices were raised. The house was like a ticking bomb.

At the beginning of term Emily retook her exams and failed them just as badly as before the summer. I agreed with school to engage a tutor to help her with study skills, and her Maths, but I was not overly optimistic. Frankly, I think that school had given up on her by this stage as she was pretty much on last warnings for behaviour.

The skiing was still going well, even though she had neglected her fitness training over the summer. Again she made the Surbiton ski school team and did quite well at Chatham, the team then going forward to the National Finals in Derbyshire. We drove up with our friends Jo and Alex, spending the night in a small hotel before the racing on the Saturday. Emily was not talking to me and spent the evening in a screechy and silly mood. Jo and Alex were pretty shocked but kept quiet about it.

I was in charge of scoring during the racing and was pleased to be away from our school group of parents and competitors. It was becoming embarrassing to be Emily's mother – she was all over the place, overexcited and far too loud. Not a hint of focus on the racing ahead. Her first run was great – fast and slick, and the team was doing well, lying in second place behind Lady Eleanor Hollis, a rival school that was near to us at home. Emily's second run, however, was a disaster. She was very uncontrolled and did not complete the run. As a result our team was disqualified. Everyone was furious with her; it was such a stupid thing to do, totally thoughtless. At least if she had finished the run the team's first time had been impressive and they still stood a chance of finishing well. But to be disqualified was truly awful. The rest of the team had trained hard and were terribly disappointed. More than that, they had had enough of Emily messing up. She made no effort to apologise and seemed not to care. That did it for the trainer, who decided that he would not continue training her. She was dropped from not just the team, but the ski club as well.

To be honest I would have found it hard to face all those people at the ski slope on Fridays. I had really had enough of ferrying her here and there, then having her refuse to train or put in any effort. The whole enterprise was pretty costly too, with racing skis, the constant waxing of skis, boots for feet that kept growing, and the training. I felt she just did not deserve to be given any more chances. Nevertheless, I was also sad as this had seemed to be the only thing that she was doing well.

Frankly, this became the least of my worries anyway. Quite a number of Emily's old friends had now fallen away and she was finding company with a crowd that I did not know, and was fairly certain I would not like. She seemed to be taking crazy risks with her own safety, not just with the places where she was hanging out, but also with boys. I knew she was drinking and smoking dope and was concerned about what else she was up to. Curfews were regularly ignored and I kept hearing worrying bits of gossip from the parents of kids who saw her out and were appalled by what she was doing.

At home, we had ceased to connect, although I did continue to try to talk to her whenever I saw an opportunity. But she would generally blank me out, or just leave the room. She spent most of her time at home on the computer, chatting to friends on MSN and on the phone. Her music had become loud and rebellious and she showed no respect for anyone else in the house (or the neighbourhood). Her bedroom, the bathroom and anywhere else she went in the house looked like a rubbish tip and, instead of homework; she became addicted to every single soap on television.

There was also a lot of not coming home from school but going to meet her new friends. Often she would tell me that she was staying late at school and, although I knew she was probably lying, it was simply exhausting trying to keep up with her. Whenever I did manage to catch her out she would just deny it, or laugh at me, and I was by now unable to enforce any sanctions.

It became a totally miserable existence living with this child. Looking back, I don't really know how I held out for as long as I did. Of course I had very little hard proof of what she was up to, but I was not stupid either. I couldn't go out much in the evenings as I was unable to leave her on her own for fear of what she might do. I therefore spent my evenings stewing over a glass of wine and going to bed with a book. The days I spent working on my university studies and walking the dog. I did keep up with the book club but, increasingly, I was just not enjoying going out.

At the time I felt that I was trying everything possible to rescue my daughter, but nothing was working. Night after night I stayed up with a glass of wine and a selection of CDs on the player, either recovering from some hurtful exchange with Emily or trying to find some way out of the awful mess we were in. I constantly raged against her ADHD and how it was wrecking our family. I was crying too much and was becoming exhausted. I'm certain that I was quite horrible to be with and became intolerant of Jonathan's needs at weekends. Again I felt as if everyone was allowed to have needs but me, mine were the only tantrums that were unacceptable. I was sleeping little and eating less.

As a family we clearly needed help. I tried many help lines and organisations, in addition to our regular supports such as the family doctor and the psychiatrist, but there was just nothing out there that seemed to make a difference. I suggested that we see a family therapist and Jonathan agreed. The first session was a disaster and it took a lot to persuade Jonathan to go back. We had agreed to do a couple of sessions just the two of us, to fill in some background and, I hoped, start to address some of the issues between us. Then we managed to force Emily to attend a session and it went so badly that Jonathan was asked to take a walk to cool down. Emily was totally uncooperative and it became clear that this was not going to work. I talked to her school about her seeing someone there but she just did not turn up for the appointments. It was all a total waste of time.

# Chapter 7

In mid-November, Tom came back for a short school break and, over the weekend, became increasingly unwell. I kept him at home on the Monday and let him just cuddle up on the sofa. He clearly had a fever, and I did all the usual things to look after him. On the Monday night I was woken at 1.00 am by a strange and haunting screaming which got increasingly panicky. I rushed to his room, by which time it was painfully clear that this was no simple nightmare. Poor Tom was thrashing around in his bed, flinging himself upwards, his eyes staring. I tried to restrain him but couldn't. He was burning hot and still screaming but I was unable to wake him. It was terrifying to watch – it was as if he was possessed by demons. I dialled 999 for an ambulance and then went back to his side in the hope of calming him.

I called my neighbour, Joan, to ask if Emily could spend the rest of the night with her as I did not want to leave her alone, and was not sure how long I might be. Emily, however, refused to go, so I had no choice but to leave her. Of course, as soon as we left she was on the phone to her father in Manchester. Luckily he did not pick up her messages until the following morning - he would have been worried sick. Emily also called several of her friends (at 2.00 am!) and by the next morning the rumour was that Tom was dying! I had a flood of calls from concerned parents to deal with when I finally got home.

The ambulance arrived in record time and within minutes we were on our way to the hospital. Tom was beginning to come to and I just held him and tried to reassure him. He was quite clearly frightened. He wasn't sure what had happened but it was pretty scary being carried into an ambulance and racing off into the night with the lights flashing. The paramedics were great with both of us.

I spent the rest of the night by his bedside while doctors and nurses came and went and tests of various kinds were done. He was given a large dose of antibiotics and became calm, but was too scared to go to sleep in case it happened again. By 7.30 am he was looking a lot better, and by 9.00 am the test results had ruled out all the nasty things it might have been. However, he was diagnosed with a fearsome virus, reported in the newspapers as claiming the lives of several young children. I immediately phoned his boarding school to alert them, in case he had passed it on to another child. In fact, another pupil had contracted the same virus after coming back to school from Asia, and we realised that Tom must have caught it from him. Finally Tom's temperature dropped to a reasonable level and the hospital allowed me to take him home.

Although Tom started to recover I continued to worry about him.

He was afraid to go to bed in case the same thing happened again and I was unable to sleep all night for the same reason. Emily's nose was out of joint as I had been so cross with her for her late-night phone calls, which had caused so much drama; I was also deliberately ignoring her and looking after Tom.

On the Thursday of the same week, a patient of mine, who was at high risk of committing suicide, reached a crisis and I needed every inch of myself to try to do the best I could for him. Although I was by now totally exhausted from lack of sleep I somehow managed to get through the day, engaging the help of my patient's doctor and holding an emergency meeting with my supervisor to make certain I had done all that I could for him. Emily chose this day to not come home from school and when she eventually turned up I was totally unreasonable with her.

Later that evening I learned that my patient had gone missing and, in fact, he did not surface until three months later, at which point he was referred to a hospital for inpatient care. However, at that point I truly feared that he had succeeded in his threat to kill himself. I felt totally inadequate as his counsellor and could not bear the thought that somehow, if I had been more experienced and less exhausted by my own affairs at home, I would have been able to prevent it. I had been unable to eat properly for several days and then I drank too much wine. By 2.00 am (that magic hour in the night!) I had managed to convince myself that I was responsible for what looked like the death of my patient.

My son could have died this week and my daughter hated me. Where the hell was my husband?

I felt all the weight of the past months come crashing down on me. I tried listening to music and, rather unwisely, sat listening to songs that reminded me of better times. I cried and cried and cried. I really felt that I just could not go on anymore. I was angry with Emily for being so bloody hard to live with and I resented Jonathan for abandoning me to deal with all this shit by myself.

Still unable to calm down, I managed to talk myself into the idea that life was just not worth living. I felt so alone, in a life that had become impossible to deal with and felt that I was failing in every single direction. At this point, Leonard Cohen, famous in my younger days for his depressing ballads, was on the CD player and the song 'Bird on a Wire' took on a sinister meaning for me. I just wanted to be free of all this mess. I had tried my best but had only succeeded in making everything worse. I wanted to run away but I knew I couldn't ever do that.

I allowed self-pity to take a hold on me. I recalled a day when I was ten years old and we were living in Pinner. My mother and I had gone into Pinner Village on some errand and she, who was at that time in despair over my father's affair with his secretary, told me she was leaving us. She also told me where she was going but swore me to secrecy. When the other grown ups began to realise she was missing I kept hold of my secret and hid in my room in case anyone guessed. It was not until the next day, when everyone was in turmoil, that I admitted what I knew. I felt like a traitor to my mother, but I was frightened that I might never see her again. Why did she not love me enough to take me with her? I was angry and confused.

And now, in my own home, I seemed to be considering making the same mistake with my own family. I adore my son and could not do that to him. I knew that if I left he would carry that forever, as I did. Where the hell was my husband? Why was he not here? Why could he not help me to deal with all this? Why was it always left to me? I was also angry with Emily. I had tried to make her life as normal as possible and all she could do was spit in my face. If we had never had kids Jonathan would be with me now. Yet if we had never had kids we would never have had Tom.

I was certainly drunk by now, but I was also out of control at a point from which I could not return, and it was a very frightening feeling. My heart, which had been pounding in my chest for hours, now felt as if it would explode. I felt a huge panic rising up through my body and suddenly was gripped with a searing pain across my chest. I doubled over as the pain increased and I could now feel a strange tingling in my left arm. 'Bloody hell,' I thought, 'I'm having a heart attack. I'm going to die!'

My memory of what happened next is sketchy, but I do recall struggling to the phone and calling my Dad before I blacked out. My father must have called my saintly neighbour, Joan, because as I came to I could hear her at the front door. We kept keys for each other's houses in the event of an emergency, and she let herself in and found me weeping on the floor. I was by now seriously frightened, although the pains in my chest had subsided, and kept feeling I was about to black out again. I vaguely recall her making tea and talking and putting me to bed.

The next couple of days passed in a fog. I slept mostly and have faint recollections of people coming into the bedroom and then going away – my father, my stepmother, Tom holding my hand, and then Jonathan. I felt I could not speak, but I really had nothing to say. I wept a lot and pretended to be asleep if anyone came in. I felt totally dead inside.

The worst thing was that I did not seem able to shake off the feeling that I was losing my mind. Everything around me felt surreal, swimming wildly around, and I just could not get my feet back on the ground. I was weepy and pathetic and had to concentrate hard just to swallow. All my bones ached, and I felt very ill indeed.

On the Monday Jonathan (who had not gone back to Manchester) took me to the doctor, but I could not put two words together sensibly and he had to explain, as far as he could, what had happened. I remember crying a lot and the doctor saying I needed absolute rest. He gave me a prescription for something called Diazepam. Jonathan also took me to see my therapist. I could not speak to her either. I was totally incoherent.

It was agreed that I should go up to Manchester with Jonathan for a few days to rest. Dad and Sue stayed in the house to look after Emily, and Tom, now fully recovered, went back to boarding school. Jonathan must have cancelled everything in my diary, as I was incapable of doing so, and we drove north.

I felt extremely fragile, shaky and panicky. It was as if all the stuffing had come out of me – I was a rag doll. Jonathan was wonderful and caring and I felt guilty for feeling so angry with him, but I still was. Our lovely flat felt serene and secure and I just lay about the place sleeping and trying not to think about what had happened. Ironically, in my role as Trustee of the Hyperactive Support Group, I had taken part in a recent radio recording, and I tuned in to listen to the broadcast on Radio 4. I sounded like Margaret Thatcher, but at least I got across the point that families with hyperactive children need help and are not getting any.

The drugs and the rest began to have some effect and I decided to go out for a walk in the city – a little window-shopping and to satisfy my sudden need for cigarettes (I had given up smoking eight years before). I felt totally weird, as if everything was happening behind a glass wall and I could not feel any of it. I wandered into the new Harvey Nichols in Manchester city centre and somehow it was all too much – the bright lights, music, confusion of shoppers, noise; I felt every person in there was invading my personal space – and I panicked. I retreated back to the flat, once more afraid that I was losing my grip on things. I began to worry that I had lost my old self for good.

# Chapter 8

Slowly things seemed to get back on a more even keel, but I realised that I had reached some sort of limit of endurance that night, and a sense of fragility remained with me. I was persuaded to take a break from my studies and I knew I was not steady enough to continue to see my patients. I completed my work assignments for the semester at the university and hoped that I would pass so that I would not have to re-do this part of the course. I saw my tutor and director of studies and we agreed that I could defer for a year. I went home to try to get myself together again.

I was embarrassed about what had happened and became rather withdrawn from my social life, although I continued to lean heavily on my closest friends for support. Without these wonderful people I don't know how I would have gone from day to day.

I was now smoking, not eating properly and drinking wine again, although with greater control. Evenings were such tough times and nights were even worse. I knew I was very depressed and was back on Prozac, but I just couldn't think of anything I could do to change things.

Emily continued on a downward spiral of her own. Not only was she treating her family badly but her friends and boyfriends too. She refused to accept any limitations and many of the rows ended with her slamming out of the house. Her father met the same response when he was home at weekends. He was becoming a seriously angry person, railing against everything, his daughter, his lot in life. I was back managing the family as before and trying to keep a lid on my own anxieties. I was drifting slowly but steadily away from Jonathan and had less and less energy to help support him as Emily needed more and more as I attempted to keep her from coming to harm.

Apart from that one night in November, I had never ever questioned my love for her, even though she was really testing me the whole time. I loved her enough to really put myself on the line now in the hope of saving her from going down in flames, even though I knew the cost would be high. Emily had learned all the right buttons to press to upset each of us and she pressed them relentlessly. She would goad Jonathan to the point where he would lose his self control and would sometimes end up hurting her, which would give her an excuse to exit the house. Often she would only go as far as her friend's house nearby and that was always my first port of call in tracking her down. God knows what they thought was going on in our house and they always took her in. Sometimes she would refuse to come home, but at least we knew where she was.

I was aware that the rows between Jonathan and Emily sometimes became physical but I did not intervene. I excused him on the grounds that she was provoking him, but deep down I knew it was wrong. I went into a state of denial, refusing to get involved and hiding from the scenes. I was beginning to feel totally powerless over the situation. It felt as if one step to the left or to the right and we would be engulfed by a storm.

In early December we were invited to a Christmas drinks party at a neighbour's house and Emily was due to be collected from a friend before we left, but she was not where she was supposed to be and neither of them could be found. Once again, what could we do? We went to the party with both our mobile phones on and just had to wait for her to call in. We had tried all the usual places but had run out of ideas and people to call. By ten o'clock we still had not heard from her and we were getting worried. We went home and tried calling around again. The friend she had been with had been collected by her father and was by then at home. Emily had apparently gone off into Wimbledon with a gang of boys the friend did not know, she could not give us any names or any idea of where they were headed. Her mobile phone was still switched off.

By midnight we were beside ourselves with worry and decided to call the police. They came quickly and relayed her details on their walkie-talkie so that a search could begin, then we sat down and gave them some background. They asked to see Emily's bedroom. Instantly, my anger evaporated. In the midst of the chaos that was now her bedroom; her bed was covered with photographs – of us on holidays, of her school friends, of other friends at parties – all neatly arranged, edge to edge, like a summary of her life in pictures. Jonathan and I were devastated. The police called back to their base and changed their instructions from trying to find a missing person to looking for a runaway. We let them have a photograph of Emily and they searched her room for any clue as to where she might have gone and what she may have taken with her.

It was a parent's worst nightmare. All the newspaper reports of runaways I had ever read came to the front of my mind, together with every ghastly outcome that I could think of. As usual, I was reduced to a weeping wreck. My fear was that they would never find her if she did not want to be found. I felt as if I was watching a TV cop programme and empathising with 'the distraught parents'. It was the worst night I had ever spent.

The hours began to pass. I had last seen Emily at lunchtime. It was now after 4.00 am. How far could she get in 16 hours? She could be dead by now.

Jonathan and I kept in close contact with the police throughout the night. A new shift of police came on at some point and we had to go through it all again with them. There was still no sign of her. Somebody the police questioned had seen her in

Safeways' car park early in the evening. They gave a couple of names but they were guys we had never heard of.

By morning there was still no news. Then, just before lunchtime, she walked boldly into the house as if she had simply been to the corner shop. I nearly burst with anger and relief. She looked OK, a bit dishevelled, but there she was. She had not run away.

The police came by to interview her and at last we were able to put together where she had been for the last 24 hours. She said she had met up with some 'friends' and had only gone to a party. When it got late she went back with a crowd to someone's house and stayed the night there. She got a bus home. What was all the fuss about? The police told her just exactly what all the fuss was about.

While Jonathan went to cool down, I tried to talk to her. Emily was not listening. She asked me to take her somewhere to get the 'morning after' pill. As upset and exhausted as I was, I called a help-line and got some information. We would have to go to St Georges Hospital, Tooting, where they had an emergency clinic on a Sunday. I got her out of the house and went straight to the hospital. It took a long time. We waited four hours to be seen and then a further two hours while they found a doctor who could confirm whether or not this pill would interfere with her stimulant medication for ADHD. Eventually, the consensus was that it would have no effect. She took the pill. And we went home.

She showed no remorse and there was no let up in her bad behaviour. As far as the police were concerned, she came from a good family so this was probably a one-off, although they did say they would have to make a report to Social Services. Once again I felt totally powerless to do anything other than grounding her and, even as I was telling her that she was no longer allowed out without our consent, I knew that she would just climb out of the window, over the garden side-gate and be off down the road.

Emily couldn't face school on Monday and refused to go in. Unfortunately, when she went into school on the Tuesday she was something of a celebrity. So many families had been woken up on Saturday night in the police search for her. By the time she came back from school she was full of praise from her classmates for her daring, which fuelled her courage to take another step, and then another, and another.

Less than two weeks later we had a repeat performance, this time the night before we were due to fly out to South Africa for a family holiday. There was a very real chance she would not be found before we had to leave for the airport. Luckily, this time we had some clues. I had confiscated her mobile phone and the police were able to follow up on the telephone numbers stored on her SIM card. By nightfall she was still missing and I decided that she was simply being malicious – she knew we were all going away and how much the rest of us were looking forward to a safari adventure. I decided to make plans with my neighbour for her to keep Emily if she turned up too late to travel with us. The idea was that she would then contact my father and Sue.

But the police found her in time and threatened that if she was not home in one hour they would come to arrest her. She came back, furious that we had 'got her into trouble with the police again'.

This was not a good way to start what we had planned to be the holiday of a lifetime. Jonathan and I had always longed to take the children on safari. We had had to book flights a year in advance so that we could use our free 'air miles', and we had planned everything very carefully so that we could get the very best out of our experience of South Africa.

The safari part of the trip was magical – all I had ever dreamed it would be, and more. For a few days I lost myself in leopards, elephants, rhinos and lions, stunning sunsets and suppers in a courtyard around an open fire. I even had the thrill of finding a leopard tortoise watching me while I showered outside. The whole experience really appealed to my sense of adventure and I felt a million miles away from the troubles of the past years.

But the rest of the holiday was a rollercoaster of good times and bad. The children together can be a nightmare at the best of times, but on this holiday they excelled at winding each other, and us, up. Jonathan's moods were frequently murderous and I played peacemaker with tight lips! I spent the night of Christmas Eve sobbing uncontrollably at how awful our lives had become, and by the time we reached our friends in Hermanas, I wanted to kill the lot of them. A cliff walk with Ruth, where I suggested that we just keep walking, helped me to steady myself, but I was slowly being consumed with anger and helplessness.

On our return I made some serious New Year's resolutions - the main one was not to let this situation overwhelm me as it had in November. Even as I made it I knew that there was nothing I could really do to stop it and I was truly frightened at the lack of control I now had over my life.

Almost as soon as the school term began we received a letter from Surbiton High School expelling Emily on the grounds that they really felt that it was the wrong school for her. They felt (and I think it was fair) that they had done all they could to help her but her behaviour, frequent truanting and her refusal to do any work in this, the first year of her GCSE courses, made it impossible to keep her there. They did, however, give us a term to find her another school.

I wasn't at all surprised. Although I woke her up for school each morning she would often refuse to get up and I could not physically get her there. She would stay in bed for most of the day or watch a bit of daytime television until 4.00 pm when her friends got home from school. From then on it was hours of screeching with laughter on the phone with them. Sometimes she would fake illness; sometimes she couldn't even be bothered to do that.

I found that I was rowing with Jonathan more and more at this time. I felt he wasn't helping me to deal with Emily, and was always grumpy when he came home at weekends, looking for quality family time and finding chaos. I felt that Emily was not the only one blocking me out – he was as well. Looking back I can see that we were floundering, trying to deal with a totally impossible situation, and taking our failure out on each other. I knew he had an important job in Manchester, and that it was very demanding, but I felt that I was fighting a nuclear war at home. How dare he be upset that he wasn't coming home to a loving wife and two rosy-cheeked children running to greet him?

One Sunday, while I was cooking the traditional Sunday roast, our tempers flared, over something trivial I suspect, and before Jonathan could walk out, I did, in my slippers!

I drove around Richmond Park for ages. I felt in danger of cracking up again and had one of my panic attacks (now a familiar feeling, but never again as bad as the night I thought I was having a heart attack). I ranted and raved at the trees. How was my life such total shit? I was sick of trying to deal with it and sick of crying. I felt that I was spending half my life angry, trying to keep a lid on everything so no one outside the family could guess what was really going on, and bloody crying. I had had enough.

Once I had calmed down a bit I decided that I was not going home. I would go and visit my friend Debbie, one of Emily's godmothers, in Sheen. Luckily she and her husband, Simon, were there and we spent the day talking and talking. Eventually I agreed to meet Jonathan in Richmond Park to talk. I told him that I would only come home if he agreed to find Emily a place in a boarding school. I said that I was sick of calling up potentially good schools and being rejected by them, but that I was also unable to live with her any more – I would lose my mind if it went on much longer. He agreed and I went home, not happy, but having at least passed on one of my burdens to him. The fact that I was also angry and resentful of his moods was left unresolved.

Jonathan, Emily and I seemed to have become locked in some sort of negative triangle. Emily and I would have a disagreement and she would phone Jonathan with her version of how totally unreasonable I was being. I would then be put into the position of having to justify what I had said and done, constantly under pressure to respond to each of her lies in order for Jonathan to have some idea of the truth. Jonathan then tried to play judge and jury. As a result, I was constantly feeling undermined by both of them. As I became less reasonable over the next few months so this sense of being undermined grew stronger and more invasive. It felt to me that Jonathan acted as if he were intervening between two naughty children. All too often this left Emily with increased power over us both.

I never doubted that Jonathan loved us all. He was constantly trying to find ways to fix the situation and he always acted with the best of intentions, but I still felt that I needed more support from him. Not only was he absent physically, but our telephone conversations also seemed to indicate that he was unable to engage with the reality of what was happening at home. He started to take Emily's side in our rows, expecting that I could be adult about it, but I couldn't be, and he did not seem to understand that that simply gave Emily more power. He was always concerned with maintaining her self-esteem, but I felt it was at the expense of mine. He put increasing amounts of energy and emotion into attempting to reason with Emily, but I already knew that we had all moved beyond the bounds of reason.

The issue with power, I thought, was becoming dangerous. Emily had always had an overriding need to exert her power and control, even as a small child. Now I saw her brandishing these skills over her father, her brother, her friends, and me. She had learned that if she 'lost it' big time enough then there was no one who could contain her. I suspected that her need for power and control had its roots in her ADHD, which is characterised by a lack of self-control and chaos in the brain, but I had always been sympathetic to this. Throughout her life I had protected her from her lack of self-control – fighting her battles for her at school, at home, within the family. I was like a lioness protecting her vulnerable cub. The problem is that she had learned that, whatever the cost to me, I would rescue her, and therefore she did not have to be responsible for herself. Of course I can excuse my actions on the basis that I did it out of love. Emily had always demanded more love than anyone could manage and, because of what I perceived as the ADHD burden on her, my love for her grew and intensified to an extent where I was unable to draw the line accurately between her wants and her needs. She ended up with a larger share of me than was reasonable, and it was at the expense of Jonathan and Tom.

I became increasingly resentful that I was living with a daughter who was a total monster, and a husband who relied on me to sort things out but, in return, was grumpy, morose and angry whenever he came home. Any time I tried to talk things through he would react as if I were attacking him and blaming him for what was going on. Whichever way I put things it became impossible to say anything negative at all. As a result I slowly withdrew from him altogether.

One of the worst aspects of this time was an overwhelming sense of being alone. Doctors, and Emily's psychiatrist, were too remote and either unable, or unwilling, to help. I felt reluctant to lean too much on my friends – we all led busy lives and I felt there was a limit to what I could expect in terms of tea and sympathy. Also, what I was going through now was beyond their experience. My father and stepmother were extremely supportive but they lived in Gloucestershire. On a day-to-day basis they could not be there, although they were always comforting and knowledgeable at the end of a phone whenever I needed them, day or night.

Consequently, I felt totally isolated, and never more so than in the middle of the night when I couldn't sleep and would imagine everyone else tucked up peacefully in their beds. All my negative energy would kick in at this time and I would rail against a God I felt had deserted me and cry along to all my old favourites on the CD player.

# Chapter 9

★ ✭ ★

Emily was getting to me more and more and I was becoming less and less tolerant. She rarely spoke to me, other than to be confrontational whenever I challenged her. I even tried writing to her, telling her my feelings and why I was so concerned about what she was doing. We had hit a brick wall. Whenever we argued she would simply use her mobile phone as a means to set up escape plans. I had lost my patience, as well as my ability to exert any authority over her. Jonathan and I agreed that the phone was a major problem. My preferred option was to confiscate it permanently, but he disagreed, on the grounds that she needed it to keep her safe. I argued that it didn't keep her safe at all, it just allowed her to disconnect from us, by turning it off. We compromised. She could have the phone at weekends, but had to hand it to him on Sunday evening.

Sunday night came and, after a major row over Emily's refusal to give up her phone, Jonathan left it to me to get it from her and stormed off back to Manchester in a rage. I was incensed with them both – with Jonathan for once again not exerting his authority over her and leaving it to me and with Emily for her bloody mindedness. I decided that enough was enough. I rushed into the study where she was on both the house phone and her mobile, holding two different conversations, plus she was on the computer talking on a chat room! She fought me like an animal, kicking and screaming, but I managed to wrestle the mobile from her. Previously, when I had taken her phone by force and hidden it, she would retaliate by either stealing it back or 'borrowing' a friend's phone when they got an upgrade. This time there would be none of that. I wrenched the back off the phone, took out the SIM card and broke it in half.

Emily threw herself into one of the biggest rages I had ever seen. She followed me around the house shouting and hitting me. I was terrified of her. She was by then as tall as me, bigger and stronger. She seemed to know no bounds in her fury and, not for the first time, I thought that she was really mad, mentally ill. Things were so wildly out of control that I called my friend, Linda, to come round and talk to her. Linda ended up taking her home with her and took charge of getting her to school the next day.

I had another sleepless night, as I began to question seriously whether she was going insane. She seemed to have stepped over some sort of invisible barrier between being out of control and becoming frenzied. What had once been mood swings had become so exaggerated that I no longer felt that they had any limits. She was either hysterical and violent or lethargic and morose. I knew that she was binge drinking (vodka shots) to the extent that she would boast to friends that she had no memory of the previous night at all. The next day she would be unable to get out of bed.

Emily seemed to have lost touch with reality. It was clear that she didn't like herself, but she was also very promiscuous sexually, frequently with strangers. She didn't seem to care what happened to her and was taking serious risks with her own safety. Our bad experiences with our daughter were piling up, and she didn't seem to be bothered about any of it.

We had become aware of a boy she knew, who she claimed was the older brother of a school friend. They had, in fact, got to know each other through the Internet, and one day I was shocked to discover that she had sent him photographs of herself, dressed provocatively. On closer investigation I discovered that she did not know him at all. In spite of confronting her with the dangers of Internet dating she continued to correspond with him and even arranged to meet him. She was often on the phone in the middle of the night and, by chance, we intercepted a call meant for her. There was no doubt that the call was from this chap, John, from the Internet. There was also no doubt that he was not a fifteen-year-old boy but a very rough-sounding adult.

Emily's social plans changed by the second, and it was very hard for us to make arrangements to do anything because we could not be sure where she would be. On one occasion we had all been invited out to supper with close friends but, at the last moment, Emily refused to come with us, so we left her at home. We got back at a reasonable time, having had a lovely evening. I

119

could sense something was wrong even before we had parked the car. We glimpsed several shadows as they ran from the house, which was ablaze with lights. The back door was open and there was a lot of scuffling in the garden and over the back fence. Jonathan went upstairs to find Emily, who had not answered when he called out to her. I took a look around the ground floor.

The whole place was a mess, as if a group of teenagers had gone on the rampage with the intention of defacing our home. There was spit up the walls, cotton wool balls had been dipped into something red and used as ammunition in a paint-ball style fight and the remains of Durex bombs clung to the furniture. Empty bottles of vodka and gin (from our drinks cupboard, as I discovered later) were strewn about and everywhere was sticky with fruit juice. Footprints covered our cream sofa and something had been smeared onto Jonathan's Porsche in the garage. There was no permanent damage, but we felt that thugs had violated our beautiful home, intent on spoiling it.

Jonathan, meanwhile, had discovered Emily, who was doing a very poor performance of being in bed, asleep. I went up to talk to her. She was clearly drunk, and I decided that talking was a waste of time. I sensed that something else was going on, but couldn't quite put my finger on it. I asked Jonathan to go and investigate. Suddenly I could hear Jonathan in a total rage, and a lot of thumping around, before a body came hurtling down the stairs, closely pursued by Jonathan. I only just recognised the boy as Jonathan thumped him, and literally kicked him out of the house. Apparently he had been in bed with Emily and must have hidden in the large closet when I went up to see her.

We were both furious with Emily, that she could be involved in trashing our home, and that she could not only go to bed with this boy but hide him as well. That she could lie so defiantly and then had the nerve to be angry with us about it all. I was beside myself with anger. I marched upstairs shouting at her. How dare she? Emily, unfortunately, laughed in my face. I hit her hard. Her insulting behaviour seemed to know no bounds. She was totally beyond any kind of reason. Later I deeply regretted hitting her. I had done the very thing that I was so angry with Jonathan for. How could I stoop so low?

I was, at this time, also struggling to understand what was happening with Emily's medication. She and I were in regular contact with her psychiatrist, but there was no doubt that the different forms of methylphenidate we had tried were just not working. Emily's violent mood swings gave concern that she might be suffering from Bipolar disorder and, if that were the case, she was on totally the wrong type of medication. It was not a stimulant she needed, but the opposite. You can't just switch from one to the other, but we agreed with her psychiatrist that she should try a different class of medication, Depacote, in the hope that it would help to even out her moods and improve her self-control.

All my life I have seen myself as a very strong and highly resilient person. I have had more than my share of dramas and crises and I have always been able to cope. One of the ways I have kept a grip on things was by putting on an appearance that I was fine, even when I had to bury some really difficult stuff. This ability to 'throw a switch' on my problems had become finely tuned over the years and was a very effective way of keeping myself together on the outside. The problem with this technique is that the stuff you bury in this way, because it has not been dealt with, comes to the surface when you are really challenged.

Now I was reaching the end of my tether. Emily acquired yet another mobile phone from somewhere and we were getting the call charges on our credit card statement. She was no longer bothering to even pretend to go to school and thus my whole day was spent dealing with where she was. She had decided that I should 'get out of her home' and I was losing the will to contain her any more.

We wrestled over the illegal mobile phone and she stormed off, threatening never to return. Frankly, for the first few hours I didn't give a damn, but eventually I had to resort to the police once again.

After the usual process of bringing her home I was left with the feeling that the police were getting fed up with us calling them out. But I couldn't think what else to do. This time they referred the case to Social Services and I contacted them myself in anticipation of finally getting some real help. I was bitterly disappointed to discover that nothing much could be done in our case. I had honestly reached a point where I felt I could no longer parent this child.

On the night of Thursday 20th January I decided I had had enough. All I could see for the future was total despair. I was not only depressed, but had finally lost hope of being able to survive this chaos, which was now my entire life, 24 hours a day. There was no respite. When Emily was in the house, it was either full-on hysteria, or an oppressive silence, both of which gnawed away at my heart. When she was not at home I worried about her. It was as if she had totally eaten me up until there was nothing left. I hated Jonathan for leaving me like this and felt completely trapped.

Looking back, I can see that I had not only lost all my sense of direction, but I had also lost myself. Everything had become so painful that I could no longer connect with myself. I felt that I had been swallowed up, until there was nothing left. I was useless, powerless – a total failure. I could no longer find any consolation in the good bits of my life; everything was too bleak and dark. God had definitely written me off. I could feel my soul cave in.

Tom was safe at school; Emily was at Olivia's house, refusing to come home until I left; Jonathan was at some work dinner in Manchester. In the company of my adoring black Labrador, Harry, and with Leonard Cohen on the CD player, I took a knife to my wrist. Managing only superficial cuts, I fetched a razor. This was not a lot more successful, but I did manage to produce quite a bit of blood. Instead of being pleased with my efforts I was instead overcome with a feeling of desolation and self-pity. There was still a place left in my head where I knew that I needed some real help. I called Debra, then sat on the kitchen floor and wept.

Debra came very quickly. What I had done had no need of medical attention, but she called the emergency doctor anyway. She then sat with me well into the night and I gradually began to calm down and realise what a pathetic and stupid thing I had done. I felt very embarrassed and foolish for making such an idiot of myself and for causing her so much trouble. I have known Debra since Emily, and her son, were born, but had never really confided in her as her husband was constantly away from home and she seemed to have enough on her plate already without my whining. She was great that night and I will never forget her help and care.

Finally, at 4.00 am the doctor turned up. The night had become surreal anyway, but neither of us was prepared for this doctor. I was feeling better by this time and all we really wanted to do now was to go to bed and sleep. This strange-looking man listened carefully to what had happened, and why. He prescribed heavy-duty sleeping pills, which I knew I would never take, and then he lectured me. Drawing on his African spiritual background, and his extraordinary religious beliefs, his advice was that Emily needed to be exorcised of her demons and I must bring her to his church for redemption. Debra and I sat in silence and listened. We did not dare catch each other's eye in case we fell apart laughing and embarrassed the poor man. His conviction was total and he was genuinely trying to save our souls.

Eventually Debra managed to manoeuvre him out of the house. He had certainly chased away the day's demons but not in the way he might have hoped. We just collapsed in a heap laughing hysterically. Every time we thought about what the doctor had said we just burst out laughing again.

The following day I felt very fragile and ashamed. In the cold light of day I just could not forgive myself for what I had done. I desperately wanted help. I continued to see my therapist once a week, and the hour we spent together became a time in which I kept trying to get my head around what was happening. The problem was that the focus remained on Emily, and how to get through the next drama. I was always able to avoid looking too hard at myself. Everything I thought and did related to Emily. I did not feel I was even a separate person anymore. Her issues were so huge that there was no room for anything else.

My panic attacks had returned, with a vengeance, and I was getting to sleep only with the help of a bottle of wine, which put me in such a dead sleep that I would wake up aching from head to toe and afraid to face the day. I truly believed that I was losing my mind and I was very deeply afraid. Once more I was staring into the abyss.

That night Jonathan came home. I hid my bandaged wrist inside a sweater but Debra had called him, so he knew what I had done. He must have been very upset but, as so often happened, an Emily crisis took up any space we might have had to talk about it. In any case, the last thing I wanted to do was talk about it. He and Emily had a terrible row about something - I don't even know what. I hid in my bed, trying not to hear his rising anger and her belligerence. They came to blows and I knew that, as her mother, I should have intervened to stop him hurting her, but I didn't. Inevitably Emily slammed out of the house. Once we had established that she had gone to Olivia's house and was safe I went to sleep.

When I awoke the next morning I was shaky and fearful. Jonathan was in a bad mood and I was relieved when he went off for a haircut. Standing in the shower I decided that if I didn't get out of here now I was going to burst. I threw a few essentials into a bag and left the house. Jonathan had taken the car so I walked round to Marion's house to ask her for some homeopathic rescue remedy (she is a homeopath, amongst other things, and a very great friend). I could hardly get my words together to explain myself and she could see that I was falling apart. I don't understand why, but for some reason I was afraid that Jonathan would catch me running away and there would be some dreadful outcome. I had ceased to make any sense at all, even to myself.

We decided that I needed to get away somewhere safe for a few days to think. I was in no state to be on my own, so it had to be with someone I was close to, but where Jonathan could not find me. Before I had left home I had written a note for him – a list of arrangements that had to be carried through (Tom to be collected from school at 5.30 pm, for instance) and I had been very careful to say that I was safe, and not to worry, I just needed some 'time out'. Within the hour I had been collected, by another friend, also a Debbie – altogether I have five friends named Debbie!

The friends I stayed with were shocked that I had reached these depths of desolation. They were also worried about my health. I had lost over a stone in weight and my clothes were hanging around me. I had kept the smoking a secret and my nerves were shot to pieces. All I wanted to do was to sleep. Sleep is such a great refuge. My bed has always been my hiding place from the world.

A doctor friend, Jan, came round to check that I was OK. I still had some Diazepam left over from my last crisis so I took that for a few days. Otherwise I slept and tried to start eating properly again. My friend had, for a long time, been trying to persuade me to see an acupuncturist, but the idea of yet another prop in my schedule had not been appealing. I felt I was spending enough money on my therapist, apart from that needles worried me. However, I now allowed myself to be coerced into seeing one. The whole experience was not what I had expected and I found it surprisingly nurturing. I also began to be aware of what all the stress was doing to my body. In terms of energy I was now running on empty. All my systems were shutting down as my body was forced to exist permanently in fight/flight mode. This explained my ability to exist on very little food and sleep and partly accounted for my being unable to feel any emotion at all. It was explained to me that it was as if I had been in a massive car accident. Well, I certainly felt I had been in a major collision, though not with a car.

I came out of the session feeling very different. It was amazing. If I had been told that the effects would be so dramatic I would never have believed it. After several sessions I noticed my quality of sleep had greatly improved, I no longer woke up aching with exhaustion, my shoulders, frequently locked in pain, began to relax and I began to be more hopeful that I would not only survive, but perhaps would not lose my mind after all.

Although I could have done with more time to rest, there were pressing issues at home. I had telephoned Jonathan several times to make sure that he knew I was OK. I blamed Emily but I knew it was about us too. I just could not go there right now.

While I was away Jonathan did his best to try to find some solutions. I think he was also worried that Emily had far outreached any of the normal teenage boundaries and something had to be done. He tried very hard to get her seen by a psychologist, who could review her ADHD treatment programme and give us some advice. It seemed that whichever way he turned he could not get any real help, in spite of referrals from the psychiatrist and our family doctor. I was not surprised – I had been trying for years and had drawn a blank. He also started to progress on the school front. I was by now adamant that it must be a boarding school.

In his frustration with the National Health Service, Jonathan decided to explore a private clinic in Kent and made an appointment, which I had to attend with them. The idea was that Emily would be reassessed with a view to her becoming a residential patient for a while. And so my brief escape came to an end. We drove down together; our expectations high that at last we would get some real help with Emily.

Our meeting with the consultant was a farce. He did not appear to have read all the reports carefully prepared for him by Emily's psychiatrist and wasted too much time on covering issues that we knew were not relevant. The issues of physical abuse and my breakdown overshadowed the causes and he seemed unable to distinguish the wood from the trees. As I had met quite a few people in his profession over the years, and was now studying psychology myself, I had to restrain myself from challenging him. Four hours later we were no closer to getting the help we needed so much. We were all upset and Emily refused to come home with us afterwards. We dropped her off at Olivia's. Jonathan and I went over the details of our meeting and we both seriously questioned the consultant's assessment of our situation. We made a formal complaint against him and it was eventually agreed that we would pay his fee to a charity.

Jonathan eventually secured a place for Emily at Frensham Heights School in Surrey, starting after half term, so I only had to get through two more weeks with her at home. During this time we met on two occasions with a social worker sent by Social Services as a result of our fairly regular use of the police. She came to our house and, on her first visit, Emily refused to see her. She returned the following day and finally got Emily to talk to her. What Emily said was a total muddle of fact and fiction but the woman was experienced and was able to work her way through our stories. She could not promise any help but she agreed to try to get Emily seen by a specialist within the National Health Service.

Emily had been waiting for a while to have an operation on her toe and it seemed a good time to get it done before she started at her new school. I desperately wanted to reconnect with her before she went away, so I tried extremely hard to be loving with her. However, it was a one-way street and I got nothing back. After her day in the hospital she was supposed to come home to rest. She had had a general anaesthetic and the toe would be painful for a day or so. I invited her friend Sammy round to entertain her.

Tom was home for half term and I was keen to spend some quality time with him to make up for going away. I wanted to reassure him that I was OK, and that I was not planning to run away again.

What should have been a quiet evening became yet another battlefield. Arriving back from the hospital we found two guys on the doorstep. Emily had invited them round. I tried to lay ground rules for their visit and said they could only stay for half an hour. During that half hour more people came to visit the 'invalid' and then even more sneaked in without my knowing. Finally Tom announced that there were now fourteen people in the house – I knew only three of them.

I kept asking them to leave, but Emily advised them to just tell me to fuck off, which they did. They were a rude and arrogant bunch, mostly boys, all of whom were bigger than me. I began to feel under siege in my own home. They took over the downstairs, turned up the music and Tom and I were forced to retreat to my bedroom. I was hesitant to call the police – we were doing that too often. Luckily Emily's friend, Sammy, who was downstairs, took a call from her parents who realised that all was not well. Her mother, Linda (who I had met through the girls and had become a great friend to me), telephoned me to see if everything was all right. It wasn't. Her husband, Steve, was around like a shot. He took control of the situation and within two minutes everyone had left the house. A big, strong man with a loud voice, clear instructions ('Out!') and a baseball bat in his hand worked wonders – he was amazing.

# Chapter 10

★ ✪ ★

With the prospect of Emily going away to school, I began to dream of getting my life back, and spending some time in Manchester with Jonathan, hopeful that we could repair our tattered relationship. I set about ordering school uniform, sewing on nametapes and trying to enthuse Emily about the idea of going. She, however, had decided that she was not going to Frensham Heights.

Emily was due to start her new school on Sunday, 22$^{nd}$ February. The plan was that Jonathan and I would take her there after we had taken Tom back to his school, which was nearby, and would be able to settle her in. I made a special family meal before we left. But then, once the car was loaded with all her school stuff (I had packed for her because she had refused to participate in the process) she simply dug in her heels and refused to go. Several scenes later, Jonathan ended up physically forcing her into the car. She screamed all the way down the motorway to Tom's school in Sandhurst. He was as sick of her antics as we were, and tried many times to shut her up, but with very little success.

Finally we got her to the school, by which stage she had calmed down and pulled herself together. By the time we had settled her into her dormitory she had made friends with the other four girls and we left with a huge sigh of relief.

Over the next few days I could hardly believe how well she was settling in. She seemed to be very happy, was making friends and getting involved in the school activities. I even began to relax a bit.

My old friends, Janette and Bob, from Los Angeles, were planning a trip to Italy to visit their son, who was spending a semester in Florence as part of his college course. The timing was perfect. We could all spend a weekend in Rome, then go on to Florence. Jonathan was only able to come to Rome, but that was better than nothing. He loved Rome, and we had some happy memories of spending time there together, pre-children.

Janette and I go back a long way – we met in Venezuela, where she had been brought up, and where I lived for a couple of years after university. Her sister and I had met in Caracas and we had become close while I flat-shared in Bella Monte with a guy she was dating. We were part of a crowd that included a mixture of white West Indians from Barbados and Trinidad, a guy from Cuba, a couple of wayward Aussies and a few Venezuelans, and we lived a very bohemian lifestyle, working as English teachers in an institute in Alta Florida. My relationship with Janette became ever closer over the years, and her family are like a second family to me. Janette met Bob, an American from California, while she and I were flat-sharing in London some years later. They have been very special friends to me ever since. We had spent holidays with them while we lived in America, and they had been over to England a few times for family reunions with Janette's English relatives and other holidays, but I had not seen them for two years, and was really looking forward to it.

We spent a wonderful week together, joined in Florence by another friend from our time in Venezuela. We did lots of cultural stuff, things I had always wanted to do but never got around to, and an awful lot of messing about in cafes. I had not laughed, really laughed, so much for a long time. It was a total breath of fresh air holiday and I returned to England feeling much more optimistic about the future.

But while I was away, things at Frensham Heights had not been going well. Emily was happy enough, but the school wasn't. Her behaviour, in and out of class, was completely unacceptable, she had violated several of the cardinal rules of boarding house life (including going out at night after lights out) and they were beginning to question whether they would be able to keep her. After just two weeks at the school they were putting her on a last chance and asked if Jonathan and I could go down to talk to her.

I really hit the ground with a bump! Only two days after my return from Italy we drove down to the school to read Emily the riot act. We took her to a local pub (the only place to go) and tried to talk to her. To begin with, Jonathan tried as hard as he could to reason with her, but all he drew from her was a complete blank. This made him so angry and aggressive that he became abusive and bullying. Emily did her usual trick of getting up and walking out, and I told Jonathan he must go and bring her back. I could see that they were both losing control, so why did I do that?

Some time passed and they did not return. I moved to the window and looked up and down the street. They were a short distance away and I watched Jonathan as he grabbed her and shook her like a rag doll. I stood in total disbelief. I could no longer deny that Jonathan was not only hurting her, but that he was treating her with a complete lack of dignity and respect. Emily broke free and ran off up the road. Jonathan returned to the pub. We tried to talk, but I felt as if my heart had turned to stone.

We went back to the school and Emily had not returned. We sat and talked with her housemistress and eventually she tried to sneak in through another entrance. She was very upset and refused to see either of us. We had no alternative but to leave. Jonathan, who had returned from a business trip to the States that morning, was jetlagged, tired and emotional. The day went from bad to worse, as I could not forget what I had witnessed and he must have been feeling very bad about what he had done. You could have cut the atmosphere with a knife. A friend called me, and Jonathan kept butting in on our conversation. This was something he did frequently and I found it infuriating. I was particularly angry that day because I felt that between Emily and him I was in constant demand, I couldn't even have a telephone call without being interrupted.

Jonathan has a very jealous nature, and I have always felt that he expects me to behave badly and go off with someone else. Once, when we were in Mirabel skiing with Jules and Charles, we spent New Year's Eve with some friends of theirs in a restaurant. Somebody's husband, well-known for his antics, but not to us, made a play for me in a bar after dinner. He refused to take 'no' for an answer, but I escaped back to our group and stood very purposefully next to Jonathan. That should have been an end to it. Jonathan, however, sensed that something had happened that night and stupidly I told him the full story the next morning. He went totally ballistic, accusing me of leading the guy on, and then threatening to go and 'cut his balls off'. He was foul to me, and I was so embarrassed that Jules and Charles and the children were able to hear his ranting, that I left the apartment. Jules came after me and Charles talked some sense into Jonathan. His lack of trust in me made me feel bitter, and suspect that I was not good enough.

Thus, when he interrupted my telephone call with a girlfriend and then challenged me, based on all sorts of ridiculous assumptions he had made from snippets of conversation that he overheard, I just blew a fuse. He hurts our daughter and then accuses me of having an affair! I was furious and, in my anger, I told him to get out of the house and not come back. Of course he didn't go and that made me even more determined that he should. In my, now unreasonable, state of mind, it was yet another example of him constantly trying to dominate me. By then there was so much anger in me, which had been building up over many months, even years, that I stood my ground.

Jonathan still refused to go. He was not taking me seriously, and I am sure he felt that he could talk me out of it, as he had in the past. But I was done with talking. He spent the night alternating between being distraught and upset, and accusing me of having a secret life that I deliberately kept him out of. I simply refused to talk. Again and again he asked if I was having an affair, and every time he did so, because it represented such a lack of trust in our relationship, I became more certain that our marriage was over. The following morning he left.

Strangely, although I went through every imaginable emotion several times a day during the week that followed, the feeling I remember most was one of relief. Watching him hurt Emily was somehow a defining moment and I really think that I just switched off my heart to him. In the past, Jonathan being upset was something I found very hard to deal with. On the one hand he had every right to cry, but there was a bigger part of me now that felt he was pathetic. I lost my respect and compassion for him that weekend. I realised that all his emotion was simply a form of bullying, and this time it wasn't going to work.

Jules came over from France that week and we met for lunch on the Wednesday. Jonathan and I had both confided in her and she was the only person who knew he had left. In spite of her attempts to encourage me to avoid making any firm decisions at this point, talking about it with her just confirmed my resolve that the marriage was over.

There was very little time to think straight about anything. The next day I received a call from Frensham Heights explaining that Emily had been caught in the dormitory in the middle of the night, drunk, with a boy. The headmaster had been called in and they were both suspended, pending a review of their behaviour. I drove down to the school to pick her up. I had a tense discussion with the headmaster and housemistress, and was left in no doubt that she was likely to be expelled. Too many things were going wrong. Her behaviour in school was so bad that several of the teachers were refusing to have her in their class. One subject teacher had not even met her yet. She was skipping classes and generally riding roughshod over all the rules.

We met with the local Community Mental Health team who, having finally been persuaded to treat her case as urgent, could do nothing for her except offer some counselling. Since Emily refused to talk to anyone this was really a non-starter. The frustration of having to deal with these stupidly inflexible people was really getting to me. Until Emily took heroin, or broke the law, their administration and procedures kept them safe from getting involved. They always seemed to have a way to absolve themselves from giving us any help with Emily at all. If she had been bleeding no doctor in the world would refuse her treatment but because she was 'bleeding' in her head they could get away with doing nothing!

I knew that I could not deal with Emily at home at this time. She was simply running wild and I was left picking up the pieces. My father and Sue agreed that she should go and stay with them while I tried to work something out. They arrived on a Friday evening, prepared to take her with them on the Saturday morning. Emily decided she was not going to go with them and took off. The police were called and, once again, she was forced to come home under threat that they would go to fetch her. When I thought the dust had settled I took the dog for a walk – my strategy for calming myself down (he was the most frequently-walked dog in the world!) I returned only to find a police car back at the house. Emily had tried to make an escape and, in trying to prevent her from climbing out of the window, she had fought with Sue and threatened her with an iron doorstop. Sue had come off worst, with a damaged knee, and was in shock that Emily could do such a thing. We were all at our wits' end. The police suggested that Emily spend the night in a police cell, and we even considered it – that's how desperate things had become.

Clearly Dad and Sue could not now force Emily to go with them to Gloucestershire and I was left considering other options. In the end, Jonathan's parents came up trumps and she went reasonably willingly to their home in Somerset.

For some time now I had been deeply concerned that Emily's medication was having very little effect and that, added to the binge drinking, had made her behaviour almost psychotic. I also suspected, but had no real proof, that she was taking drugs of some description. Too many times she had been totally bombed after a night out and her face was looking bloated and grey. This might also account for her violent mood swings. I was not convinced that she had been taking the Depacote properly while she was at Frensham Heights and felt in a total muddle about the whole prescription drugs thing. Nothing seemed to be working, and I no longer knew what to do. Jonathan, who had always questioned my decisions on drugs anyway, felt that it would be a good idea if she came off everything so that we could see what she was like without any meds. Being in Somerset with his parents, and no other influences around her, seemed like the best time to try, so she came off all her medication during her stay with them.

Tom came home for the Easter holidays and I was determined

that he should no longer have to deal with all the drama surrounding Emily, as well as my relationship with Jonathan. Now twelve years old he was quite wild, but also extremely sensitive and I was concerned about how he was dealing with everything. He was very close to his father and to me. It was important that he was not made to compromise his feelings in any way.

With Emily in Somerset we were able to spend some quality time together and I made sure he met up with his local friends as well. He seemed to be coping all right and was relieved not to be doing battle with his sister. One of his techniques for coping during the last few months had been to escape into computer games. While this obviously concerned me, it seemed to work for him. Now he seemed more willing to do other things. He played golf with friends and appeared happier than he had been for a long time.

Jonathan's parents could not keep Emily forever, so I had to think of a way of managing her back at home. A friend, Claudia, who has a weekend house in a small village in Wiltshire, suggested that we go there for a week, where I could try to get back on a more even keel with Emily, and she would not have access to her social life in Wimbledon.

The cottage is in the lovely village of Hindon and was such a perfect place to be. Tom and I spent a few days there on our own, then Dad and Sue came to visit and to stay overnight.

Jonathan's parents were bringing Emily up for the Easter weekend and we would all have lunch together.

Jonathan had always insisted on protecting his parents from the reality of life with Emily, so they had very little awareness of the events of the past few months. When we did see them Emily was often quite reasonably behaved. They love her dearly and she loves them. Betty and John knew that I had initiated the separation from Jonathan and, although I had always had a very close relationship with them, I now felt I could not talk to them. The distance between us was very hard to bear, yet I realised that they would automatically side with their son. Consequently the day was a difficult one, and I was grateful that Dad and Sue were there.

My good friend, Ione, also came to stay during that week and we had a wonderful time catching up and just being together. We walked and talked and drank too much wine. It was great. Our friendship goes back years to when she was my boss at a PR agency. We then went on to run our own business together until I went to live in America. Finally the time came for her to leave and Emily, Tom and I were on our own.

Emily had kept her distance, and had been reasonably manageable, but she and Tom were back to their usual game of winding each other up. Tom was becoming far more confrontational with her. He had grown a lot and was less willing to put up with her bullying. They came to blows on Easter Sunday morning and he really thumped her. Emily just broke down. I sat with her for hours trying to comfort her. So much had happened to her – expelled from one school, seeing consultants at a mental hospital, interviews with social workers, not to mention her parents' separation. I really tried to let her get everything out of her system, to open up and give us a chance to talk. Top of her mind was that her brother had really hit back (until recently she had been able to dominate him) and he had hurt her. She just felt that all anyone seemed to do was to hit her. Chillingly, her take on the situation was that her father had a right to hit her.

For the first time in many months we actually talked and for me it was such a relief. Somewhere inside her was still the girl I loved so deeply. She had just got so far down a deep black hole that she couldn't find a way out. She knew she was hurting everyone but she was also hurting just as much. I have always said to her that I am there for her whatever happens. For a long time she had been deaf to anything I said, but this time I really felt she heard me.

Through all these terrible months, no matter what she did, and even though I might rail against her, my love for her had remained untouched. No matter how foul she was to me, a lot of my tears were because I love her and want to help her get through this awful time. I had never stopped telling her that I love her; she had just stopped believing it.

On this day I really thought that something in her had shifted, and I hoped she could hang on to the idea that things do not have to be this way. I vowed to her that I would never give up on her. There was a better path she could take and I would help her take it. For the first time in ages she let me hug her and I was overcome with joy.

Less than ten hours later Emily was back in combat mode and I was utterly at a loss as to how to react. She was totally unreasonable, and it seemed impossible to draw back to where we had connected that morning. I can't remember what set her off, but she exploded, and I was her main target. She shouted and screamed at me that she was glad her Daddy and I had split up because I was such a bitch and only pretended that I loved her. None of her ranting made any sense. I couldn't even figure out where all this was coming from. Once again I felt very scared that there was something really serious going wrong inside her head. She was so on fire that I became frightened.

I called Jonathan and asked him to come and get her, as I had no way of coping with her like this, and felt it was time he took a turn. He agreed to come down the next day. Emily refused to go to bed and sat up watching a movie on television. She kept stoking up the open fire and I didn't dare go to sleep in case she set the place alight.

Jonathan arrived the next morning determined to resolve things. He and I went for a walk to talk privately and I could feel that he was desperately trying to find a way through this mess. He had received a letter from Frensham Heights to say that Emily had been expelled, so again she had no school to go to. The tone of his conversation led me to believe that he thought I was not handling the situation properly, and that it was up to me to rebuild my bridges with Emily. I was supposed to 'repair' my relationship with her.

It became clear that Jonathan had no intention of taking Emily back to Manchester; after all, he had to work and could not look after her during the day. I suggested he take some leave but, inevitably, after long talks with Emily, he left without her.

That evening we drove back to London, dropping Tom off at his friend's house where he was spending a few days while he and Alex did a rugby camp at his school. Emily and I went back home.

# Chapter 11

*★*

Instead of falling apart, I was filled with a determination to rescue Emily somehow. I accepted that I was now truly on my own, and was convinced that Jonathan and I were better off apart. I would never go back to him. The problem was, what could I do for Emily? Simply finding another school did not look like an answer. It seemed as if we had reached a point where something dramatic had to happen in her life in order to allow her to climb out of her black hole and become less self-destructive.

Back in March, there had been a series on television called 'Brat Camp' about an outdoor therapy programme for young people in the States called 'Redcliff Ascent'. The programme claimed to 'provide an impacting, therapeutic experience that leaves the youth with a new inner strength and air of confidence, a new appreciation for parents, home and family and a renewed commitment to work hard to overcome weaknesses while magnifying strengths'. The kind of kids they took, and had huge success with, were those with emotional and behavioural disorders including substance abuse, depression, defiance and problems with authority, ADD and ADHD.

Several people called me about the series at the time, and my stepmother recorded a couple of the programmes which followed a group of teenagers while they hiked around in the deserts of Utah, building camps, making fires and learning survival skills. At the time I had been hopeful that getting Emily into a boarding school might engage her in a different lifestyle and that might be enough to turn her around. It was clear that she needed some sort of containment. The boot-camp concept seemed a violent thing to put her through and I worried that she might crack up on such a programme. I couldn't bear the thought of sending my lovely daughter off into the wilderness.

Now, however, the idea of a therapeutic programme seemed the only way forward. She had effectively dropped out of school, and all we had was the prospect of her just going off the rails at home, with all the consequences of that for her, and the rest of the family. I didn't think any of us would be able to cope. Something else had to be done to break the downward spiral. But still the boot camp felt like a step too far.

I went onto the Internet to see what other programmes there might be that would be more appropriate for Emily. I also sought advice from her psychiatrist, and got Janette and Bob involved in gathering some information from the States. At this time, my favourite aunt, Valerie, who lives in California, came over for a visit with my cousin Karen. We talked on a regular basis so she was up to speed on what was happening. They also offered to do some research for me. It transpired that my cousin's adopted son, who has ADHD, eventually went to a boot camp, so Karen was extremely helpful.

There is a funny thing that my experience during this time has taught me. There is no such thing as coincidence. Whenever I felt that I was at some important crossroads in my life, chance events occur at just the right moment, and throw up just the right people who send me off in a new and important direction; in this case, my aunt and cousin. Here was some really valuable advice and support, and yet I would not have thought to ask Karen. And how come that the television programme on Redcliff Ascent was broadcast just a month before I needed to open my mind to the possibility of really different solutions?

One of our family mantras is that you get out of life what you put in and now I was giving my all. I could be totally focussed. The time for thinking and talking had passed and I was ready for doing.

I gathered up a mass of information on a whole range of programmes and it became apparent that one alternative to Redcliff would be a special school which Emily could attend for a semester. This offered similar therapeutic support, but would be less challenging than the wilderness programme. My cousin Karen's knowledge, and her research, were critical at this point because if I had taken this option I think that Emily would still be there. Another cousin, Jonathan, put me in touch with another person who was invaluable. Catherine had been through a similar crisis with her daughter and was much farther down the line than I was. Her support and encouragement at this particular moment gave me the courage and belief that only a 'tough love' approach had any real chance of success.

Thankfully, with Tom away at his rugby camp and Emily avoiding me like the plague, I was able to give my full attention to finding the right place for her. While I worked obsessively, putting plans in place for her to go away, Emily did what she liked. There was no longer any point in beating myself up for not being able to contain her. We were far beyond that now.

Tom came home for the weekend before school was due to start for the summer term. On the Saturday night I took Emily and a couple of local friends to a party in Surbiton. Somewhat ironically, the host of the party was the same guy who was unceremoniously ejected from Emily's bed and thrown onto the street by Jonathan. Another parent had agreed to do a pick up at 11.00 pm and I curled up for an evening with Tom. By midnight there was no sign of Emily and her mobile, as usual, was switched off. Eventually she called in and said they were all invited to spend the night. Emily had told me earlier that the boy's parents would be there and, although I had long since stopped believing a word she said, I just gave in. To be honest, I knew that if I refused to let her stay she would anyway. So I turned over and went to sleep.

Emily called me again at 5.00 am telling me to come and pick her up. She said that they were all up and had had breakfast, but that she didn't want to stay and help tidy up after the party. I told her to call me again when they had finished clearing up. She called at 8, 9.30 and finally, at 10.30 am, she said that they had finished cleaning, so I agreed to collect them. I drove down to Surbiton and found them dancing in the street in front of the house. There was no doubt in my mind that they were all very drunk, possibly stoned. Their clothes were ripped and dirty, one guy had no shoes, and Emily showed off a number of horrifying bruises and scrapes. Why did I not go and confront the parents? Because in my heart I knew there were no parents there. She was safe, and that was all that mattered to me. The truth had no way of coming out at this point anyway as she was on a different planet and was unable to string two words together sensibly.

I took the other boys home, one to Wimbledon, the other lived around the corner from us. When we got back Emily went straight to bed, but not before I glimpsed what looked like terrible scrapes all up her back.

Emily's friend Sammy had also been at the party so I called her mother, Linda, and left a message asking her to get back to me urgently. It was four hours later that I heard from her and was able to piece together the events of the night before. Linda and Steve had received a call from the police in the middle of the night saying that they had arrested Sammy and several others from outside the party. A gang of yobs from Kingston had tried to gatecrash the party and had caused £9000 worth of damage to a neighbour's car. Emily had then let them in through a window and they had invaded the house.

Linda and another parent had been back to the house and had spent much of the following day trying to sort out the mess. What had been done to that home defies belief. There was ketchup and all manner of stuff smeared up the walls, across paintings and up curtains; the contents of the freezer, mixed with soups and tinned food was all over the floor and furniture; the place was littered with empty bottles and overflowing ash trays and the front bay window was smashed and had to be boarded up. The parents had not been there and were, in fact, away for the next week, having left their sixteen-year-old son at home alone. It transpired that Emily had been out of the house when the police arrived, but that a number of other people at the party had given her name to the police.

When Emily finally emerged from her bedroom I demanded some answers. She denied any involvement and her recollections of the night were totally confused. Most worrying of all was that she genuinely seemed to remember very little about it. She was not just throwing out lies; she had huge blanks about where she had been and what she had been doing.

She seemed totally bewildered, and the terrible scrapes and bruises she had made me concerned that she might have been raped, but she really didn't seem to know.

It seemed as if Emily was on some sort of moving staircase – whenever you thought she had done the worst thing possible, that some sort of limit or boundary had been reached, she went to the next level. There was a serious risk that she could be prosecuted for what she had done this time and I decided that I just had to get her away from here.

I took Tom back to school later on that day with no idea that I would not see him again for a long time. When I got back I called Jonathan.

Jonathan was very supportive. We were beginning to accept that our best option was for Emily to go to Redcliff Ascent in Utah, but there was a waiting list for a place. We decided that I should take her over to the States and wait for a place to become available. He took on all the paperwork for her registration, got the psychiatrist's report together and handled all the details. Janette and Bob invited me to bring Emily to Los Angeles where we could stay with them, and they could help me to take her to Utah as soon as a place came up. Redcliff knew she was now an emergency case and were going to do their best to get her in quickly. Jonathan booked flights for the following Saturday.

All these plans were kept secret from Emily, as I knew she would just run away if she had any idea of what was about to happen.

Emily had left her passport in France while on a school trip. The school had managed to get it back but I needed to go to Frensham Heights to pick it up. Before I left Emily on her own at home I thought it would be sensible to keep my own passport with me just in case she was wise to anything. It was missing from the drawer in which we kept important papers and, search as I might, I could not find it. Emily denied all knowledge of course (it was found a few months later, ripped to shreds and stuffed down the back of a sofa). This was Thursday and we were due to leave in two days' time.

In a state of panic I went to the Post Office to get a form for a new passport and bumped into a neighbour, Adele. She is a lawyer and the best possible person I could have seen at that moment. She immediately offered to help rush through a new passport and helped me to get the necessary papers together. I drove down to Frensham Heights to collect Emily's passport and to talk to the headmaster. He was very kind, and promised to help us find Emily another school to return to after the programme.

Friday I spent at the passport office in London and, with Adele's help, managed to come home with a new passport. On Friday night Jonathan suggested delaying the flights until we had confirmed a place for Emily on the Redcliff programme.

I had reached the point of no return. I felt overwhelmed by the last few months of chaos, confusion, pain – even insanity. There were no more options left to us and I was on automatic pilot – like an oil tanker ploughing through the water towards its destination, completely unable to change direction.

Jonathan came down from Manchester to help me get Emily out of the country and I fixed supper for the three of us in a daze. Tom was, blessedly, in school for the weekend and safely out of the way.

There was very little interaction between us during the meal – nobody felt like eating. I couldn't trust myself to swallow, and the impending conversation hung heavy between us all. Jonathan finally picked the moment to tell Emily that she would be flying to Los Angeles the following day to spend some time with Janette and Bob while we found a new school for her. I don't know what else he could have said; there was no easy way to say: 'Look, you are going to 'Brat Camp' because we can no longer cope with you!'

But Emily was not stupid. She was not going to be taken in by this sop. She shoved her chair back and headed towards the door. Jonathan tried to stop her, and I feared another fight, but she managed to wriggle free and got out of the front door. This time we could not risk her going far. We thought she was likely to go to her friend Olivia, so we called Olivia's parents and explained the seriousness of the situation. Olivia admitted that she knew where Emily would go.

We paced the kitchen, hoping to give Emily time to calm down before calling the number that Olivia had given us. We knew that it was for a house around the corner where she was hiding out with the guy who, only this week, she had referred to as a boyfriend. She was there, but refused to come home. We imposed a midnight deadline and said if she was not home by then we would ask the police to fetch her.

The deadline came and went, and nobody was answering the phone – I was terrified that they had gone out, or that she had moved on from there. As usual the police were very understanding, and by 3.00 am they were on their way to get her. We needed to be at the airport by 10.30 the next morning for a midday flight.

To distract myself, I threw things into cases so that all we would have to do was fall out of bed and into the car in the morning. Finally, the police arrived. They had had to threaten to break down the door before Emily agreed to come quietly, but now, thank God, she was under our roof.

I don't remember much about the rest of the night. I can't imagine that either of us slept as we were both on total red alert in case she tried to make another escape – using her old route out of her bedroom window, across the roof, down into the back garden, over the gate and off. We both felt that this might be our last chance to get Emily the help she needed. We couldn't afford to miss this plane.

Eventually dawn arrived and we woke Emily with the intention of arriving at the airport early. She refused to get up. We tried to remain calm; keeping our voices even, but it made no difference. She quickly spiraled into a rage of defiance and this time her anger took me with her.

There was nothing on God's earth that was going to stop me getting her onto that plane, there was too much at stake. I tried to keep my cool, but gradually found myself losing it. By now she was totally defiant, screaming and shouting. I dragged her out of bed, planning to force her to get dressed, but she fought her way past me and into the bathroom, locking the door.

Jonathan tried to reason with her, talking in measured tones through the bathroom door: 'Sweetie, Darling...'. His conciliatory tone was totally ineffectual and, as time leaked away, I found I could no longer keep a lid on my emotions. He pointed out that there was no way we could physically force her onto a plane, so he would have to cancel our flights. But I was not prepared to give up. This fourteen-year-old girl was wrecking her life, and ours. Drugs and alcohol were her escape from reality and, if we gave into her now, what hope would there be for any of us in the future?

Even if her father was willing to give in to this tyrant of a daughter, I was not. I went down to the garage and hunted out tools, intent on unscrewing the lock on the bathroom door. As I wrestled with a screwdriver Emily threatened to kill herself if we got in. I genuinely suspected that she might try. There was no telling anymore what she might be prepared to do.

Having failed with the screwdriver, I returned to the garage in search of a hammer, with the idea of smashing through the door. Jonathan could see that I was losing it – the whole situation must have been very frightening for him. Months later he claimed that I had threatened to smash Emily's head in. Mad as I was at that moment, I know that I could never have done that; but I had passed beyond all normal boundaries.

I was furious that, yet again, he was prepared to give in to her. His attitude seemed totally pathetic to me. All the emotions of the last few months were now bubbling to the surface – I felt like a volcano ready to erupt. Yet if I allowed that to happen I would surely lose all reason. I have no idea just what I would have been capable of doing.

I was so angry that I tried to break down the bathroom door, screaming at Jonathan to: 'Bloody well pull yourself together and **do** something'. I had barely broken one panel in the door before he took over and kicked it in. On the other side of the door, Emily was screaming with fury and promising that she would throw herself out of the window. As the door splintered, Jonathan grabbed her and pulled her out onto the landing. He held her there on the carpet, hoping her anger would subside. As if...!

My head pounding and my heart breaking with the anguish of it all, I left them on the landing and put bags into the car. Outside in the driveway I became aware that golfers, arriving at the clubhouse opposite for their Saturday morning game of golf, must be hearing everything that was happening in our house. I suddenly felt very exposed.

How we got Emily to the airport I will never know. She wrestled with Jonathan in the back seat all the way to the airport and, to this day, I don't know how he managed to keep her in the car. It is a forty-minute drive through Kingston on a Saturday morning to get to Heathrow. In order not to crash the car, I had to use every thing I had to block out the fighting, yelling and kicking in the backseat and get us to the airport safely.

As I drove I tried to look at the options. If we really could not get her onto the plane what the hell were we going to do? Just going home and having lunch was not an option. I thought of driving to a hospital emergency unit and demanding some kind of psychiatric help – but whether for Emily or for me I was less than certain.

Somehow we got to the airport but Emily was showing no signs of giving up and checking in for our flight. She screamed at the airport police, and anyone else who would listen, that she was being taken against her will, and Jonathan still had to restrain her. I parked illegally and ran into the terminal building, looking for the Virgin Atlantic help desk. My usual good manners failed me; I barged to the front of the queue and begged for help. Without hesitation the man behind the desk picked up a telephone and called for security. Although I was calmer now I worried he might have me removed from the terminal, but instead a wonderful Virgin security guard came to our rescue.

This remarkable man grabbed a wheelchair and followed me out to the car. Jonathan had by this time managed to calm Emily down a bit. He said they had agreed that she should be allowed to go back to say goodbye to her friends and that she would come back tomorrow without any fuss. I couldn't believe it. Having got this far there was no way I was going to risk ever going through this nightmare again. I was done with being reasonable, and said so. Emily screamed again for help from the police and an officer approached the car. The Virgin security guard intercepted him and explained what was happening. He moved off.

At this point I think Emily realised that she would have to give in. There were now three of us, and a wheelchair, and she had a choice of getting on the plane with some dignity or not. While she considered the situation the security guard joked that at least he was out in the sunshine, and assured us that the flight would wait for us. Emily finally pulled on some clothes and came quietly.

The security guard took our luggage and led us to a desk in the terminal where we were checked in (even though the flight had officially closed). He then took us straight to passport control. We said a hurried goodbye to Jonathan, who could go no further. He hugged and kissed a now rather subdued Emily. They did not see or speak to each other for the next four months. Our lovely security guard only left us once Emily was firmly in her seat and had promised not to cause any more problems.

For the first few hours of the flight I was numb with shock. I became aware that the whole of my left side hurt where I had thrown myself against the bathroom door at home. My arms ached from hitting the banisters on the way down to the car and my cheek was bruised from when Emily had lashed out at me. I felt totally used up, but sleep was impossible as the scenes of the morning played and replayed in my head.

Emily plugged into her headset and sat looking away from me. I didn't care. We were on our way to Los Angeles. One of the stewards checked on us from time to time but all was quiet, we were both totally deflated.

At some point in the flight Emily leaned over and stuck one of her headphones into my ear.

'Listen', she said, 'your favourite track'.

This broke the ice between us and we started to talk. Neither of us made any mention of what had just happened, we just chatted as if we were going on holiday.

# Chapter 12

★ ☆ ★

Having fought like an animal with my out-of-control daughter I had, this time, won a physical battle. The two of us were now on our way to Los Angeles. But I knew that this skirmish was only a tiny part of the war. No matter how determined I was to save her, Emily was equally determined to self-destruct. Even though I was prepared to do anything to rescue my daughter I understood that the powers of any parent are severely restricted by the life paths that their children choose. You can only stand by, impotent, as they shoot themselves down in flames, while you pray that they will be given some moment of redemption that they will grasp with all their strength.

But, in the heat of the moment, you cannot be sure that this will happen. How can you tell what an out-of-control fourteen-year-old will do?

Teenagers are scarcely more than children, who have rushed into thinking that they are adults. Society tells them that they have a great future, but they don't know what that means, and they don't understand the responsibility of it all. They subscribe readily to the celebrity culture that is inflicted on them, and lose sight of what life is about and what it expects of them. They are lost to the value of their parents' experiences of life and are in danger of never learning how to live, how to give of themselves to make life better. They become stuck in a cycle of self-gratification, with a complete lack of commitment to developing their own lives.

I sat back in my seat on the plane, suspended over the Atlantic Ocean. I felt all used up, totally blown away by the events of the morning. The next hurdle would be getting her through US customs at LAX (Los Angeles Airport), nine hours from now.

But I need not have worried. By the time we landed in LAX (Los Angeles airport) Emily seemed to have decided that she was not going to put up a fight. Fortunately, a well-known British television actor, who had been drinking heavily during the flight, took issue with a security guard in the queue for immigration. His outrageous behaviour resulted in his arrest by the airport police. It caused quite a scene, and entertained us all while we waited patiently for our turn at the immigration booths, by which time Emily had clearly decided not to play any similar games. She smiled sweetly at the immigration official and told him she was visiting LA for a holiday. I heaved a sigh of relief and we moved through to collect our baggage without further incident.

Bob was waiting on the other side of customs and I was so overjoyed to see him that I could hardly speak. Jonathan had telephoned to warn him of the state of our departure from England and he had not been sure of what to expect, but was ready to send a rescue party to immigration if necessary.

We threw our stuff into his car and drove up the freeway to Calabasas, just beyond the LA city limits, chatting away, swapping news of our families and making plans for our 'holiday'. I had never been so glad to be there. He and Janette have a wonderful home, with a pool, and I had stayed there often enough to feel at home. More than that, I was with my dearest friends and I knew that they would do all they could to help us.

Emily was also happy to be back in LA and she behaved as if she were on vacation, eager to see Alyse, Bob and Janette's 18-year-old daughter, and looking forward to some shopping. (Shopping was not on my agenda). Bob and Janette were shocked at my appearance, thin, haggard, bruised and battered. They just held me in their arms and I felt comforted and loved.

It was so wonderful to be with them all again and Alyse, just about to finish high school, took Emily under her wing and treated her like a little sister. I was totally exhausted so, for the first few days, while Janette and Bob were at work, I just chilled out by the pool, trying to recover. Emily did not come near me at first, but when she finally came out to the poolside for a sunbathe she looked at my colourful bruises and said: 'What on earth happened to you?' 'You happened to me', I replied.

It was only two weeks since we had spent Easter Monday at the cottage in Hindon, and now here I was in Los Angeles contemplating sending my daughter away to 'Brat Camp'. While

Emily sat upstairs on the computer e-mailing back to friends in England, I was on the phone trying to figure out the best way forward. Actually, I found that, having made the decision now for her to go on the Redcliff Ascent programme, things began to fall into place at last. The people at Redcliff were accustomed to situations like ours and were very good at helping me through the process of enrolling her in their programme. After all the problems of getting Emily onto a plane from England, I was very worried about getting her to Utah, even though Bob, and Janette's sister, Julie (another of my great friends from my time in Venezuela) had offered to come with me. The programme, however, said that there was no way we should have to risk going through that again and promised that they would send someone to collect her as soon as a place became available.

Within a few days, by Monday, 3rd May, the administrator at Redcliff Ascent had a date for us, and offered that they would send a security team to collect her on May 9th. Ironically that was Mother's Day in the US!

Keeping the date a secret from Emily was essential, as I did not want to risk her running away. I also had to keep her busy until then. She was beginning to talk to me and we were spending more and more time together. I hired a car and we did a little sightseeing, spending a couple of days with Julie and her family in Beverly Hills. Julie works as a translator at the courts in downtown LA and we had the fascinating experience of sitting in on several court hearings – one involving a gangster up in court for a drive-by shooting. We also went shopping in The Alley, an area downtown where you can buy all kinds of fake designer goods. We bought a pile of gifts for friends back home and I treated Emily to some new clothes.

Back in Calabasas Alyse took Emily out quite often with her friends. It transpired that Alyse's boyfriend, Matt, had been in a lot of trouble as a teenager and came off the rails when he was about sixteen, ending up in a similar style of 'boot camp' to the one Emily would go to. He was brave enough to agree to share his experiences with us, particularly since Bob and Janette knew very little about his life before he met Alyse. After Emily went to bed one evening he sat up with us and totally opened up about his past, explaining how the boot camp had really helped him to turn his life around. He offered to talk to Emily and to prepare her for going to Redcliff. I have nothing but admiration for Matt and he helped me to have a clearer idea of what Emily would have to go through. Daunting though the information was, I really began to believe that the programme might be the answer for her.

Although my panic attacks had become quite frequent and I had a miserable case of hives, which left an ugly rash around my rib cage and my chin, I was beginning to feel much better. We went out in the evenings and I met several of Janette's girlfriends – a really good crowd. We went walking around the lake for some exercise and I was getting a decent tan from lying by the pool. I began to make plans for Sunday 9th when Emily was due to go to Redcliff.

Janette's family decided to have a Mother's Day celebration which would be hosted by her sister Julie and her family in Beverly Hills. I was particularly pleased, as I knew this would be a difficult day, and I would need some major distraction to get through it. I really appreciated the way this lovely family had always included me as one of their own – Janette's mother, introducing me to a friend of hers at a party some years ago had said: 'Oh, and this is Joanna, she's one of the family too'. Since we lived together in London, Janette and I have felt like sisters and have always been able to turn to each other in good times, as well as bad. And now, with Alyse and Emily getting on like a house on fire, it looked as if the next generation might be the same.

As Sunday loomed I began to get cold feet about Redcliff. Jonathan told me that he had had to sign a 'power of attorney' for the programme – not only were we physically giving up our child but legally too. It was a huge step, luckily taken by Jonathan in England. I'm not sure I could have signed the papers. It would have been all the harder as Emily had at last started to open up to me during our time together in LA.

For months one of my major problems had been lack of any communication from her. So much had happened, but I could only guess at what was going on inside her head. Her take on events was garbled and confused, there was so much anger inside her and she had some dangerous ideas on relationships that made me worry about her mental health. Her view on reality was distorted, as if she were seeing life through a cracked rear view mirror. It was very frightening.

Finally, Emily had admitted that all the drinking and (as I had suspected) the dope and pills she had taken helped her to forget where she was, and what she was doing. We were at last able to confront her drugs problem together. I had been through a time in my own life when I had used a lot of social drugs, so I was able to empathise with her experiences. I admitted to her that I had been in danger of wrecking my life with them, and explained that it's not just the drugs themselves, but the whole drug culture that you get sucked into: dangerous people, brushes with the law and losing control over your life. I told her that I did not want her to go through that. I had been lucky to escape any long-term consequences of my destructive lifestyle at that time, but many others that we knew were not so lucky and even ended up in South American jails. These stories, I warned, can be made to sound glamorous, but the reality is sordid and frightening. Janette picked up on the debate and, in confirming my story, added details that I had long forgotten. I think teenagers often imagine their parents have no idea of what their lives are about and Emily was clearly shocked at our knowledge and experience of drugs and sex and danger.

Emily had repeatedly refused to speak to her father on the phone since we had come to LA and told me she never wanted him to come near her again. I wondered if he had been here instead of me whether she might have said the same thing about me. I was still so angry with Jonathan that it was easy for me to promise that she would never have to see him again unless she wanted to. I tried my best to comfort and support her while still insisting that she treated me with some respect.

I never discussed my relationship with Jonathan with either child and was always careful to justify his actions to them when they were angry with him. My own mother had wounded me deeply as a child with her attempts to recruit my support against my father while their marriage broke down and I was painfully aware of how destructive that tactic can be. For years I digested information about my father that caused me to hate him, until I discovered that my mother was mentally unstable and had given me only the bits of the story that she felt certain would poison me against him. That sort of agony takes years to shift and had left some remnant of doubt about the real truth. There was no way that I would do that to my children. Our relationship should not be a cross they have to bear. At no point had I thought that Jonathan was a bad person. Our separation was more to do with protecting the children and myself from his inability to deal with our totally unreasonable situation. Neither of us could cope so, as far as I was concerned, there was no baddie or goodie in our case. I had simply had enough of dealing with Jonathan and his issues.

I had very little contact with England during this time. I called Tom at school every day and tried to ensure that he was OK. I also spoke to my Dad to let him know what was happening, but I just could not bring myself to call any of my friends. I was so tired of having to go over the events time and time again and was still in shock at the way we had left England. I felt I needed all my energy to deal with the here and now - there was nothing left to spare.

On the Sunday I woke up at about 5.00 am and opened the blinds to let the sun in. Then I took a cup of tea back to bed. Everyone else was still asleep. Usually, if I felt a panic attack coming on, I had learned that if I just gave into it, doing some yoga breathing, I could just hold on until it passed. This morning, however, they were far more frequent and I worried how I would get through the day. Above all I needed to hold on to myself today or else Emily might flip out and run away. I reflected that all this stress was really now affecting me in a big way. For a long time now I had had to hold my own emotions in check because of my fear of their effects on the rest of the family, particularly Emily and Jonathan. I thought that if I reacted as my heart dictated everyone would lose control and who knew where that would end? I was exhausted with holding myself in check. But I refused to give way today.

The girls all put on 'posh frocks' and even the boys looked smart, LA style. We piled up the car with food and gifts and headed out to Julie's house. The freeway was busy and it took ages to get to Beverly Hills. I felt like a coiled spring on the inside but somehow kept up with the girls' banter. At Julie's house the atmosphere was festive and all the mothers exchanged gifts and hugs. The barbecue was up and ready to go and the table in the dining room was heaving with all sorts of delicacies – a mixture of Jewish and Mexican dishes typical of this family. Real soul food.

Emily was like a cat on a hot tin roof and I was concerned that either she was picking up on my mood or she knew that tonight would be the night she would leave. The party was based in the courtyard of this very attractive art-deco, Mexican-style house and Emily kept demanding private time with me in the garden at the back. Lots of issues were flying around in her head that day and, looking back, we had some genuinely important conversations. I was able to let her know that I believe in her and that whatever happens I will always be there for her. We had a lot of debate about what a mother is, and what a daughter is, and I was surprised by her sudden (and timely) outbursts of really deep feeling for me. When your daughter consistently yells how much she hates you, it is easy to start believing her. But today I saw inside the little girl, rather frightened and lost. I also had to acknowledge that, even while she ranted and raged and threatened me, she needed me and would probably always need me, as every daughter needs her mother at some deep level. I will never, whatever she does in her life, reject her.

I couldn't bear for the party to be over, but by late afternoon it was time to leave. In the family group that remained of the party everyone knew our story and there was a lot of hugging and wishing of luck before we left. Back in Calabasas the plan was for Alyse and Matt to look after Emily, while Janette, Bob and I went to the local Starbucks coffee shop in The Commons to meet with the security people, sent by Redcliff, who would come to the house in the early hours of the next morning for Emily.

We met with the Nicholsons at around 9.00 pm that night, and sat at an outside table in front of untouched iced coffees. Although this ex-policeman's experience was of taking hardened criminals into custody, he had been escorting minors to programmes like Redcliff for years. By the end of our conversation I liked the man and felt confident that he would treat Emily as well as she allowed. His wife, Cheryl, also an experienced escort, seemed to be a wonderful combination of tough but caring. Bob gave them details of how to get to the house – he had already given the men at the gatehouse to Calabasas Hills instructions to let them in and out.

I don't recall much about the rest of the evening. Unable to sleep, Emily got onto the computer to email friends in England. I sat in the garden with a glass of wine and some notepaper. I wrote and rewrote a letter for Emily that the Nicholsons would give her on her journey to Utah. In it I tried so hard to make her understand that I was sending her to Redcliff Ascent because I love her, and because I no longer knew how to help her.

Finally I got into bed and lay there listening to Emily's fingers tap, tap, tapping on the keyboard while she made her last contact with her friends at home for what would turn out to be 100 days.

# Part Two – The Wilderness

✩ ✯ ✩

*And God created lands filled with water for men to live in and deserts so they could discover their souls.*

*Proverb: Tuareg*

# Chapter 13

## REDCLIFF ASCENT – OUTDOOR THERAPY PROGRAMME

The following extracts, given at intervals throughout this section of the book, are taken from the Parents' Information pack and are reported here word for word as Emily progresses through the programme:

'The Redcliff programme is directed towards communications skills, introspection and self-efficacy. These 'phases' are broken down into eight parts, the first one being an introductory phase, and the other seven travelling the traditional directions of native America. We use tribal motifs because they work well and are appropriate to the environment. Wilderness skills are used as metaphors for life lessons and experiences. A student may turn in two phases a week, making it possible to graduate in as little as four weeks. However, most take somewhat longer due to their personal issues getting in the way.

Often the students equate phase completion with graduation and, while this is a fair yardstick of performance, there are other things that must be accomplished as well. Along with schoolwork, there is fieldwork (getting along with peers, hiking well, doing their share etc.) and therapy. The student's therapist decides when there has been significant progress on the issues that caused the student to be placed here. When  these criteria have been met the student will be scheduled for the next graduation. Graduations are held every other Monday.

Along with progress towards completion of the programme, phase completion earns the student such things as spices, sweetener and phase meals.

Each day the students cook breakfast as soon as they awake. At breakfast they cook oatmeal or nine grain cereal. Then they must tear down their camp and prepare to hike to a new area where they will set up another camp. The students spend a great deal of their day hiking to a new camp. Through the afternoon they will write in their journals, write home to family, work on school phase books and learn skills such as bow-drill fires, traps and Native American Skills. The students will then cook supper and have time around the campfire to talk and write poetry.

The students also have an opportunity to have one-on-one interviews with staff members. This will help the youth and staff members to keep open communications lines, and to offer individual time to each student.

In the evening they will have a group session where they may discuss many things such as problems in the group, areas of concern or areas of praise. During these groups the staff may give the students a subject and ask them to respond to it or they will process and problem-solve as a group any problems that have arisen. The students have a lot of time to think and ponder about the future and decide if they are doing the things that truly make them happy.

At each new camp that they build the students construct a large shelter made from tarps, which is similar to a tent. This is where they sleep.

Mother Nature is able to offer a great deal of natural consequences when a student does not do what is expected. For instance, if the students are taught to build a shelter and they choose not to listen, learn and build the shelter then they must suffer the consequences, such as wind, rain or snow. They are taught how to pack their sleeping bags ('wigis') and personal items in order to be able to hike successfully. If they choose not to listen or refuse to pack appropriately, then they may carry everything in their arms until they arrive at their next camp. If they swear or use profanity, they have to pick up a small rock and carry it with them through the day.

The students eat basic, non-processed foods such as rice, lentils, oatmeal, cheese, peanut butter, trail mix, wheat flour, chicken and beef bouillon, powdered milk, nine grain cereal, refried beans, black beans and tuna fish. They receive fresh fruit, vegetables and meat once a week. They can also earn honey and spices if they maintain a minimum of four bow-drill fires per week. The students are watched very closely to make sure they drink plenty of water every day. They begin by drinking one quart of water before they start hiking.

The students each carry their own food and cooking supplies and usually are responsible for preparing their own food, then cleaning up their own utensils. On rare occasions the group may have earned an incentive meal and cook it communally.

The students make fires by using a 'bow drill set' which includes a bow, spindle, fire board and palm rock. Each student must gather their own fire equipment and this process is begun in the Polliwog group. The students are instructed on how to make this bow drill set produce a fire. This can be a long and frustrating experience for students but offers an effective metaphor for them to apply to their lives. As students are able to produce more and more fires, they are then able to earn spices, sweetener and other items that make life a little more pleasant in the wilderness.

## PHASE ONE

During this time, students are acclimatising to the altitude and the environment, learning the rules and foraging for basic tools and equipment. In this, and in all phases, they learn about values, keep a journal, write poems and original stories and do introspective assignments. They build a bow-drill set, digging stick and a spoon. Soon they will start to hike, do camp chores and roll their own pack. Each phase also has an autobiography assignment that must be signed off by the student's therapist.'

## EMILY'S JOURNAL

Emily gave me her journal to read shortly after we got back to England and agreed it could be included here. Six books scrawled in her own hand – sometimes neatly written and illustrated with little cartoons, often chaotic rampages of words which are hard to make sense of. All have been stored in her backpack, mistreated by the weather and occasionally dunked in water to the point that they are difficult to decipher. However, each word and each page conjures up the vivid experience of her life in the deserts of Utah. All the pain and fury, all the happy times, and there were many of these, and all the achievements she made while she worked her way, day by day, through the eight phases of the programme.

## DAY ONE - Monday 10<sup>th</sup> May

*This morning I woke up at the sound of my mum coming into the room. I glanced at my clock on the video machine, it was 4.05 am. I was very confused. Two other people had come into the room as well. I was told I was going to camp and I had to go with two people I didn't know when I agreed with my mum that she and I would go together and she would drop me off. But I went with no fuss with them and we landed in Las Vegas in no time. We arrived at the camp after a couple of hours driving. April (aka Mountain) met me at the door and we went through a series of testing and stripping. We also did a drug test. After all this I met Melissa and Reese. I really like Melissa, she's cool but she doesn't eat anything! Reese has a good sense of humour so he's good to have a laugh with.*

*Then after we had done all the paper work we loaded up our packs. I tried mine on and it was really heavy! We go in the car and put blindfolds on so we were dropped in the middle of nowhere with a group called The Polliwogs which is like a group that everyone goes to first to learn survival stuff before they get put in another group. I collected big rocks to use on putting the shelter together. Melissa and I talked for a bit and then we got down to some work.*

*The fire is warm*
*But I am cold*
*I miss my mum*
*But I know*
*What's best for me.*

**Goals:**
*Be positive*
*Do everything I get told with no fuss*

## Autobiography 1:

My name is Emily. I am 14 years old. My birthday is on the 6th of July. I will be 15 then.

I live in Kingston in London and I go to Frensham Heights School which is a boarding school. I've been at my boarding school for half a term now and I got suspended so my headmaster thought it would be good if I went here (Redcliff). My hobbies are, skiing, dancing and playing the flute.

Skiing is my favourite thing I like doing. Last Easter I took part in a ski camp in France (it was called The British Ski Academy). I trained there for two weeks and then I went home and went back a month later to take part in the Junior National Championship Inter-School races. I did well and got a bronze medal in the Giant Slalom. I train back in London at Sandown Ski Centre. Sandown is a dry ski slope. I trained on the dry ski slope every Friday and I got selected for the school ski team (this was when I went to Surbiton High – I got expelled from there for not doing any work).

When I went to boarding school I had to stop skiing because I was staying at school full time.

*I also enjoy playing the flute, which I got up to Grade 5 in. I also do street/hip-hop dancing at my school.*

*Things started going really wrong a couple of months ago and its all been pretty much down hill from there. When I went to boarding school I think it helped me a lot. Not fully, but a lot. I have not run away or broken any rules since then. I have had the occasional drink and smoked but I want it to fully change.*

*I used to fight with my mum and dad a lot especially when I was out of order. I tried my hardest to not come here but even though I hate it so much I think I will benefit from it. I didn't know my parents would send me to a place like this but I guess they have tried pretty much everything for me which I really appreciate.*

*I get on well with my brother who also goes to boarding school. Before he went to boarding school we used to fight a lot but now when he comes home some weekends there isn't really time to fight and I just have fun with him.*

*I really hope this programme doesn't last long because I wanna go home and apologise for everything I've done and I wanna show them I can do it!*

## LOS ANGELES

Once I knew that Emily had arrived safely at Redcliff Ascent and I had thanked the Nicholsons, I sat holding the phone in my hand wondering what to do next. Bob suggested sleep. It seemed like a good idea. It was now 10.00 am and the day was already hot. Somehow, Alyse had got up and gone off to school. Janette and Bob were preparing to go to work! We were all shattered, and not even emotional anymore. I drew the blinds against the day and crashed out.

When I awoke it was mid-afternoon and I was not sure where I was for a moment, until the events of the night came flooding back. The tapping of Emily's fingers on the computer, the Nicholsons with their handcuffs, Emily going off into the night, the phone calls from LAX airport, then Las Vegas, then Enterprise, Utah where the administration offices for Redcliff are based. I imagined her swapping her jeans and T-shirt for the brown utility dungarees I had seen in the brochure and selecting her kit from a warehouse full of pots and pans, bedding, water carriers and all the things she would be carrying around for however long it was going to be. Then off to join her group in the desert. What the desert meant I had no idea. I imagined a huge, empty landscape, hostile and unforgiving, hot and dry. I prayed she would be able to hold on to herself, whatever happened, but I could not shake the conviction that I might have sent her into something too big for her to cope with and she would surely fall apart.

I lay on my bed, thinking, for what must have been ages until I heard Bob and Janette come home. I forced myself up and into the shower.

At around 7.00 pm I got a call from Redcliff. Emily was fine and in good spirits. They were amazed at her attitude – she seemed to be embracing everything like a big adventure and was eager to get going into the desert. Having met her group – the Polliwogs, she had quickly linked up with a girl called Melissa and was instantly accepted by the group as the life and soul! As ever, my girl is Miss Sociable. Thank God.

## *DAY TWO*

*Life is so fucking bad at the moment I can't do or say anything. I miss everyone and everything. And like everyone else I WANNA GO HOME. Last night I could not get to sleep and when I did I woke up when the tarpaulin was flapping continuously.*

*Today we woke up really early and we had cold oatmeal for breakfast, which was really gross. I was feeling really depressed this morning but once we got to the doctors I was OK. I tried learning my rules again and it worked and I got most of them. When we got back from our medical I was surprisingly not hungry I am worried about Melissa because she isn't eating or drinking. But I know she is now eating and drinking a bit and doing her work.*

*I got really upset today. I don't like this place at all but I think it's the people here and what I have at home that is keeping me going.*

*My therapist hasn't come yet but he/she will come.*
*I miss everyone too much.*
*I hate this*
*But I gotta get through*
*I wanna go home*
*So much it's hard to bear.*

## LOS ANGELES

Today I went to the beach at Malibu with Leonora and we walked for miles and miles along the sand. When I am on my own I find it hard to put Emily out of my head but Leonora was a great tonic and we had a good day. Unfortunately I still could not wear shorts and a T-shirt because my bruises now looked too violent for public display, but I felt much more positive about life. At least, for now, Emily is safe and I have the chance of a break. I need to recover physically and mentally from the last months and I also must be careful to use this time to really sort my own head out and to think about the future. I feel weary and fragile, and am frequently on the edge of tears – remorse, guilt, fear, self-pity? All of those things and all at once.

## DAY THREE

*I really hate being here with The Firehawks (my new group now that I am through the survival skills stage). I can't stand it. I was getting used to being with the Polliwogs and I made friends with everyone there. I got up this morning after a really bad night. I kept waking up and because I was sleeping on the end I got soaked because it was raining so, so, so hard and the wind was driving the rain straight into our shelter.*

*I did some more phase work before breakfast. I didn't have any food for breakfast because I have been feeling sick 24/7! But then we moved out of camp and on to a different spot where we waited and then Silver came and got us and I was soo surprised when they took me and only me to another camp. I was really upset about leaving everyone because they have helped me a lot over the last couple of days, because I have been soo upset (still am) and I used to cry every minute (still do). I hope everyone in Polliwogs is doing OK because I'm doing OK I guess at the moment.*

*I'm not looking forward to the hike.*

*I wanna go home so bad*
*I miss my mum and I'm trying to cope.*

*Wind causes ash and stuff and also trash to scatter.*

# Chapter 14

★ ✩ ★

## PHASE TWO

This phase represents the direction of the east, the east is where the sun rises and so stands for beginnings. They say that the past is a memory and the future is a dream, that the present is all we can really know. That means that each moment is a new opportunity to start over, to change your life into something more pleasing to you. The value of the east is courage, an appropriate trait for those who wish to begin something. Many think that courage is the lack of fear, but that is not true. True bravery is doing what is right even when you are scared, or in spite of what others may think. The colour of the east is yellow, which is a warm, golden colour that signifies good purpose and abundance. It also stands for the yellow races of humans. The totem of the east is Raven. In the wild, ravens, along with magpies and crows (the Corvid Family), are among the smartest of birds. They are alert, wise survivors. Skills learned in this phase are; camp cooking, low-impact camping, flintknapping (stone tools), basic health and hygiene and making pine pitch glue.

### *Autobiography 2:*

*I think my mum is the bravest person I know. She has been through so much over the last two years and she hasn't given up at all!*

*I started playing up and fighting with her about a year ago and it's all gone down hill from there.*

*I got chucked out of my first school and she freaked out totally and when my behaviour got worse and worse and she was too tired and anxious for me she had a nervous breakdown. That's when I started going to boarding school because my mum couldn't cope with me at home so I could only come back on the weekend!*

*My mum was living at home with only my dog because my dad works up in Manchester and my brother is at boarding school too. So she was living at home with only the dog so I think that is really brave of her to live in a big empty house by herself. I would get really lonely (I guess not as lonely as I am here but lonely).*

*She was having a really hard time BUT she got through it and we are getting along really well now. So she doesn't get upset when she and I are fighting because we are not fighting.*

*Courage means that you do not give up on something even it looks or seems difficult. A challenging thing like climbing takes courage to do. When you are faced with something you are afraid of or don't like doing you need courage to do it.*

*I'm really extremely scared of everything here at this camp and especially scared of not getting out of this place. I hate it here and have really learned my lesson for being bad. Nothing can be much worse than this.*

## DAY FOUR

*This has probably been the worst day of my life. We hiked five miles and it was probably the hardest and most tiring thing I have ever done. It was fine for everyone else because they have got used to hiking like that non-stop over the time they have been here at Redcliff. So today was awful for me and I really do hope that we go to bed early tonight because I'm sooooooo tired it's unbelievable.*

*What is really annoying me and upsetting me is that I can't stop thinking about my home and my mum and dad. I was sick this morning I don't know why. I just woke up and was thinking about my mum and I was sick! So I felt really sick all day. I'm also really upset that no one really likes me because they don't talk to me and they just make fun of me.*

*Also the fire tools are really hard to find and the phases are getting harder and longer. I'm finding this all too hard and too upsetting.*

*Phase work is hard*
*Nobody likes me*
*I wanna go home*
*Coz I feel like I can't cope.*

### *DAY FIVE*

*I had the worst possible day ever in my life. We hiked 10 miles and I just got too tired and could barely move my legs so everyone got really stressed at me and they were laughing at me because I was going so slowly. Another thing that made it hard was I kept thinking about my mum and going home and because I knew it is a long way away and that I might be here for a very, very, very long time and I've been here for a week and I'm still not used to anything here. Whenever I wake up in the morning I expect my dog to be by my bed and my mum standing there with a cup of tea. And all I can see is trees and stuff and I just break down and start crying.*

*I know I'm supposed to get used to this place and the hiking but I can't seem to do that because I just wanna go home desperately and I have hope but it's going to take me ages to get through the phases especially as I haven't even given in Phase one and I haven't made a fire yet.*

We had to crash camp last night in the pitch black and we saw what we thought was a 'UFO'!

When I woke up this morning I tried my best to not think about going home but it didn't work. That's all I can think about.

I can't get used to
Anything here
I just wanna go home
Or move groups

## DAY SIX

I have had a pretty good day. I have been a bit like my normal self and I think I have been accepted more into the group now and I have been getting along with everyone. I think Amanda is really quiet but she can be OK. Mark helped me by giving me advice on starting fires so did Ethan and I got smoke and black punk!! It was close but my spindle kept popping out!

We played the sign game and Screaming Viking which was really funny and it's really the first time I have laughed in a long time. After we played a couple of games we had visitors. I was really hoping it would be the Eagles coz my friend from Polliwogs went there.

*I'm getting better at*
*Not missing my mum*
*I've got lots of cuts*
*And scrapes*
*And I keep hurting my bum!*

## DAY SEVEN

*We did the Vortex today. It was extremely hard because it was going up and down these large hills. I also had to carry the group tarp. I didn't mean to be so slow and annoying to everyone but it was really hard for me. I was climbing up and I tripped and my pack slipped sideways and I just collapsed. I just started crying and crying and could not get up. It was not fun. Near the end of the hike it was mostly flat so I picked up a bit and kept up with Erin.*

*Finally we got to camp and I was put on latrine* (digging toilets) *duty, which was OK coz I think I'm good at digging sumps* (holes in the ground for all the stuff to go in!) *and stuff.*

*I feel like I have let everyone down today coz I was slow and whining a lot so we didn't make the drop* (food supplies). *So I feel like I owe them a lot. Also I think I'm getting really, really, really fat!*

*We didn't make drop today*
*It's all my fault*
*I didn't mean it*
*But it was so hard*

## LOS ANGELES

Today was my last day with Bob and Janette. I have had a good few days doing very little, catching up with Julie and her family in Beverly Hills and just hanging out. This evening a crowd of us went out for supper at a favourite Greek restaurant in Malibu and I was able to thank Bob and Janette, Alyse and Matt for all their help and support. Promises were made to keep everyone up to date with Emily's news and to bring her back to LA after the programme.

## *DAY EIGHT*

*I GOT MY FIRST FIRE!!!!!!*

*We hiked four miles today. I started off really badly and my pack fell off, so I had to re-roll it which was really stressful. After I re-did my pack I was going really fast and I kept up with the front of the group. But then my pack started slipping off my back so I slowed down a lot. I was very tired when we stopped. Then things got much better but then my bladder* (water carrier) *split!!! And it leaked all the way down me, which kinda sucks.*

*When we got to camp we set it up and I started working on my fires. Then after a few goes I got a fire! That means I was able to use my special bow that I made myself, to create enough friction to make a spark, which I then put into a nest of bark from a tree to smoulder until it caught fire. It was hard work but I haven't felt this happy in a while!*

*I hiked today*
*I hope you are pleased*
*I got my first fire*
*And now I have cheese!*

## COOMBE HILL, KINGSTON, ENGLAND

I arrived back in England and went straight home. The house was empty and I felt very weary. Luckily Perry, who had been looking after Harry (our Labrador), turned up and I was just delighted to have my dog back. He looked a bit skinny and threadbare, apparently he had been pining a lot but I hoped now he was home he would recover.

I had called Tom every day since I left and it was good to speak to him tonight and make some plans for the weekend. I had not seen him for six weeks – the longest time ever – and I couldn't wait to give him a hug. We had a good catch up of news and then I had to let him ring off.

After our conversation I just felt miserable and lonely. I put on some music and just sat about wishing things were not the way they were and then, instead of opening a bottle of wine, I went to bed.

## *DAY NINE*

*Today I turned in Phase 1! I was wanting to turn in Phase 1 and Phase 2 but I couldn't seem to get a fire and I ran out of time because I did my poo glue* (the black sticky substance produced by rubbing the stick into a stone in order to get a spark) *wrong!*

*I had a pretty good day today. I saw my therapist and we chatted about life at home, which made me realise how much I miss it. It was really annoying coz letters can't be faxed or e-mailed from England to base or visa versa so it takes a really long time for letters to go back and forth. I really wanna hear from people at home especially my boyfriend. I've never been so far away from him and it feels really, really unnatural coz we are totally inseparable.*

*I also feel so dirty. I normally have a shower, shave my*

*legs, pluck my eyebrows, colour my hair so it seems so weird.*

**Goals:**
*Try my best at tasks*
*Work for honey*

## COOMBE HILL

I spent my day making a list of all the things I will do while Emily is at Redcliff. There was a lot to think about and I had an urge to get settled in one way or another. I wanted to prepare for how things are going to be from now on and make my own adjustments before Emily comes home. I hope she will get through the programme quickly – the average time I was told to expect would be 45 – 65 days. I decided to plan for the 65 days and any sooner would be a bonus.

While I was away I had been thinking about how family life is going to be now that Jonathan and I are separated. The house held many bad memories for us all and I began to work on plans for letting it out and possibly moving to a smaller one. I needed to look carefully at the logistics of it all. I knew that the cost of Emily's programme was horrific and felt certain that I would not be able to stay here. Also, the house was now too big for a Labrador and me, and too costly to run. I convinced myself that down-sizing would make a lot of sense. We had some friends who were considering renting for a year with a view to emigrating to New Zealand and I thought this might work quite well for us. It would provide some thinking time while Jonathan and I sorted ourselves out, and in a year's time we would know what would be best for Emily's future as well.

I called an estate agent in Wimbledon to try to get some idea of the rental value of the house and discovered that Jonathan had already started this process. I should not have been shocked, as we had discussed this on the phone when I was in LA, but I was surprised that he had actually done anything about letting out the house.

In order to let out the house we would certainly have to redecorate it, as there was a fair amount of wear and tear, plus the damage caused by Emily and her rages, and of course there was the shattered bathroom door! Jonathan agreed to contact a guy we had used before at our Hammersmith house and I hoped he would agree to do the job. He is a lovely man and I felt I would rather have him around than a stranger.

I checked into costs of furniture removal and storage and felt quite glad to have a project, even though it was one that involved the dismantling of our family and our home.

I also determined to go back to my studies at the University. If I was going to be on my own I would need some means of supporting myself and I was beginning to feel the need to get my own life back again. I arranged to see the Director of Studies, with a view to picking up the course where I had left off last December. I also contacted the surgery to see if they would have me back as a counsellor to see patients there. Everything seemed to fall into place very nicely and I made plans to re-start in September.

Over the last months I had spent so much time and emotion on my daughter that I had all but withdrawn from my own life. Jonathan and I had very little life together either, with him living in Manchester all week and nothing but rows and problems at the weekends, so I had become rather insular. What I needed now was to get out and among my old friends, to be with them talking about positive things, having some fun and catching up with what was happening in their lives. I also wanted to get fit again. I had forgotten what it was like to be in control of my own daily life.

### DAY TEN

*Today was staff change. We had a good lie in this morning. My hands were really dirty from the sap from making poo glue! I'm getting on really well with fellow members of the group which is really good. My blisters on my feet are getting much worse.*

*I was very upset when Pee and Hayley left coz they had*

*done so much for me when I was struggling last week. We got four new staff – Seeking Bow, Jessica, Dan and Amy. Seeking Bow got some cactus needles and started popping my blisters. Then when we were hiking they hurt so bad I was crying. Everyone was really supportive about it though and Mark was really nice, walking with me in front and talking to me which I find really helpful.*

### Goals:

*To get another fire*
*Be more positive about things*

# Chapter 15

★ ✪ ★

**PHASE THREE**

In this phase we look at the direction of the south, in the south it is warm and comfortable, there is much play and joyfulness. It is the time of good food and prosperity. This is where we go to heal and to rest. The value of the south is self-discipline, because one needs to do what is right even when times are easy (sometimes that is the hardest thing of all). Do you know anyone who has had life so easy that they never achieved their potential? The colour of the south is red, which is a strong vital colour, it has in it the elements of adventure and life and connection to the earth. It also represents the red races of humans. The natives of the plains called the path of balance, or right living the 'Chaupa', the red road. The totem of the south is Wolf, the wolf stands for family and leadership. Wolf also is a teacher and like all good teachers, sometimes the lessons are hard. Skills learned in this phase are; plants of the great basin desert and their uses, making cordage from plant and animal fibres and hafting a stone knife.

*Autobiography 3:*

*I was born near Hammersmith so my first home was there. Our house was just up the road from where Dawn French (the comedienne) and Lenny Henry lived. I went to school at John Betts, which was walking distance from my house. I had a nanny called Anji. She was the nicest nanny I ever had and I was very fond of her and I still am.*

*I lived in Hammersmith till I was about 4 then my dad's work got moved to Washington DC so we all had to move there.*

*Washington was a really cool place (what I can remember of it anyway) then, at the age of 9 I moved back to Kingston (in London) where we have lived for the past 5 years.*

*I have done lots of things wrong that I shouldn't have done which is why I'm here. I've been chucked out of my school.*

*I used to drink quite frequently which most of the time got me in some sort of trouble. I smoked cannabis.*

*I have been grounded and then run away for a night and stayed at my friend's house so my parents have been worried sick about me so they call the police and then there would be big fights when I got home and everyone would get upset so I wasn't just hurting myself but I was hurting every member of the family. And plus nobody had time to do anything else but look after me and my problems all weekend. The things I did right were not very often.*

*I improved in school one year but then my behaviour got*

*bad. I worked hard at getting my flute done and I got up to grade 5 but I could play grade 8 pieces with some work.*

*I have done lots of little bits and bobs that were good but one thing that I'm really proud of is coming here. I know they really, really, really struggled to get me to go from England and there was a huge thing about that which made everyone really upset but when I got snagged* (arrested) *in LA I went willingly and I'm proud that I'm trying to change.*

### DAY ELEVEN

*Today I woke up and half the shelter was gone! They had pulled it off to wake us up. We fixed up our packs and I had group tarp. I know I'm not that good at hiking so I was a bit pissed off that I had it today because I have a load of blisters on my feet that I can't walk on very well because they really, really hurt. I couldn't even stand up coz it was so heavy plus we got food drop on Wednesday so my food bag was really heavy.*

*We had a two hour stop and Erin got picked up and taken to the Bullfrogs which was quite sad. When we hiked it really hurt my everything.*

### Goals:
*Bust* (get) *4 fires*
*Be positive*

## COOMBE HILL

This evening Jonathan and I had our first conference call with Emily's therapist. It felt very strange to be talking to her in Utah from London, and with Jonathan in Manchester. It was almost surreal.

These weekly sessions were our only verbal contact with Redcliff during Emily's time there and became very important to us. Through the therapist we not only kept up with her progress, but also had a chance to talk quite deeply about what went on before she went to the programme. Jonathan and I tried hard to be very honest and open during these sessions, even when it involved going over ground that we would both probably prefer to forget, but we understood that what we said would be important in the process of helping Emily. I was finding it hard to talk to Jonathan. I felt cross with him that he often took these conference calls in airport lounges, with an airport announcer in the background, even though he set the time for them to suit his schedule. Perhaps he needed these distractions as we were dealing with some painful stuff. Our conversations became increasingly difficult as we tried to discuss a number of urgent issues, many of them being aired for the first time. Our pride had to be firmly swallowed, and this was never easy.

We also got news of Emily and what she was doing, some of which was great, but was also sometimes worrying, as her spirits would seesaw from day to day, and her behaviour was erratic at best. Thankfully she appeared to be making friends and was somehow getting through the programme, but I think she was finding it difficult to face her issues. It sounded as though she was all over the place emotionally, but we just had to hold on to our faith in the process and allow it time to work.

Today we also received a photograph by email of Emily taken out at the camp. She looked so lovely – and smiling, even if she was a bit grubby! These photos arrived every two weeks and I found them most reassuring. I kept the most recent one in the kitchen so I could look at her every day. I even found myself talking to her image on occasion, particularly when I received a letter from her, which I did most Wednesdays.

Emily's letters became the highlight of my week, and if they were delayed I would be devastated, imagining all kinds of terrible reasons why she might not have written. Whatever her news, her words helped me to feel close to her somehow. I read them over and over again. Often she ranted and raved about how awful everything was and how she would die if I didn't go and get her NOW. Then there would be a letter full of little anecdotes about life in the desert, the hikes, swimming at the waterhole and news of other kids in the Firehawks and why they were there. Sometimes she sent me little gifts – I would open the envelope and there would be a wrapper from her soap bar, a special stone (which I still carry in my handbag), the sales ticket from her backpack when she earned it, a friendship bracelet (which I wore around my ankle until after she graduated). These are all very precious to me and I took them as signs that she wanted to try to reconnect.

## DAY TWELVE

*It was my mum's birthday today so I was upset not to be at home with her. I miss her so much it's actually getting to the point that it is actually getting unbearable to stand.*

*I was getting really annoyed today because I didn't get any phase work done because I was writing a 12 page letter to my dad which was really upsetting because I had to think about why I was here and what I had to apologise for.*

*Today we had a layover day and I had to soak my feet (blisters). It was really relaxing! I'm so glad we aren't hiking.*

*I'm so hungry*
*I'm homesick*
*I'm going to be so happy when I can go home!*

**Goals:**
*DON'T SAY I CAN'T*
*Try my hardest*

## DAY THIRTEEN

*I had yet another bad day today and now everyone hates me. Louise is not talking to me and Amanda is bitching behind my back.*

*I couldn't hike today because my back was absolutely killing me. Everyone was getting so pissed off with me that I just gave up and sat down so now I'm either going to be put on Quest or not going to be able to hand in Phases 2 and 3 this week.*

*We hiked 4 miles and I gave up again so we took a break. Amy tried to help me but we both got told off for it. I feel really bad now because she was crying coz Seeking Bow was being a (excuse my language) DICK FACE! He hikes too fast.*

## COOMBE HILL

It was my birthday today and I did not feel much like celebrating. I had Tom home from school for the weekend and would have been content just to be with him and forget the idea of celebration. However my brother, Peter, his wife Liz, and friends, Debbie, Adrian and Elizabeth came over in the evening and I ended up having a great time with them all. I was nicely spoilt with gifts and was really happy to see them. I even began to feel a bit more like my old self – not just putting on a face to be sociable.

Tom was lovely – I had missed him so much and I have always felt incredibly close to him. He is affectionate and sensitive and I just really hope that all this has not done him too much damage. We have always been able to talk and we were doing a lot of that now. I kept trying to reassure him that things would be OK but he seemed more bent on making sure I was OK. I must make sure that he does not feel he has to take on any burden from all of this – none of it is his fault and yet he has had an awful lot to cope with. Not reasonable.

### *DAY FOURTEEN*

*I had a very tiring day today. We woke up at like 7 or something and we had a cold breakfast. I put too much milk powder in my oats so it was gross. We set off hiking and we were going up a really steep gorge and Clare slipped down and like broke her knee or something. She was screaming for like the next 3 hours while we waited for someone to come get her. Storm Crystal, Jumping Cat and White Grizzly came and we all helped lift her out. I felt so sorry for her. Then we hiked 9 hours which was really hard but we did it.*

*I'm so tired*

*I wanna sleep*
*I wanna eat*
*And dream of sheep*

***Goals:***
*Be positive*
*Don't get upset*

# Chapter 16

## PHASE FOUR

In this phase we look to the west, it is where the sun sets and the day ends. All things come to an end and then begin anew, all things move in circles. Seasons, planets, the elements and our own lives. You think of a thing, you do the thing, you contemplate what happened (and then think of another thing!) The west is the time of contemplation, for remembering and dreaming. The value of the west is respect, one of the Redcliff Ascent (RCA) rules is to respect everyone and everything. It sounds strange and difficult at first, how can one respect everything? Yet the effect of this trait is that everything soon begins to respect you, which is very nice. The staff here at Redcliff, indeed the whole world, is kind of like a mirror and will reflect back at the student much the same thing as what they show. The colour of the west is black, which is the colour of silence, depth and the place where new thoughts and things are born. It also represents the black races of humans. The totem of the west is Bear, the tribes called bear the cousin of us all, and respected him greatly. Not just the respect of fear, but the respect of admiration and emulation. Skills learned in this phase are; basic first aid, knots, knife safety/sharpening and birds, bugs and animals of the great basin desert.

## Introspection

*In life we go through obstacles that may feel very hard but we always come out stronger. And in order to live a meaningful life to the full we need to go through all the hard bits to come out as a good person.*

*At the moment I'm going through a really hard time. But I know that once I have completed this programme I can be a better person and live a better life. I mean I will still have to go through life struggling over the many obstacles but there is also time to be happy. That's why I'm here. I want to be happy.*

### A Place in the Tribe

*I would want to be a healer. I would have wanted to help any person I could have. It would give me so much satisfaction to see a person come in really sick and then walk out well and fit again.*

*Also, a healer is someone the tribe can all rely on. People go to the healer to be healed and most of the time, except really rare circumstances where you can't be healed because it is not possible, you are healed. Healers are very important people. Also a healer is a person everyone can look upon as a really good person.*

*I came here to transform myself into a good person like a healer that everyone can rely on.*

### DAY FIFTEEN

*We hiked half a mile today. I made a new bow and sharpened my spindles. I lost my palm rock so I got a new one and made a hole in it for the spindle. I had quite a good day but because we weren't doing anything we had to pack up and hike to the water source where I played Frisbee with Seeking Bow and Sam, which was really fun. Louise was really happy today because she got her knife! And Mark got his backpack! Dave left today. We don't know why. I think we are getting a new polliwog.*

*I'm so hot*
*Can't wait to eat*
*Coz now I have a phase meal*
*I'm so happy*

**Goals:**
*Be positive*
*Don't cry*

## DAY SIXTEEN

I had a good day today except I didn't get a fire. Seeking Bow helped me sooo much and he even let me use his really excellent palm rock! I got black punk and smoke.

Also, Jade Raven came today and we talked about my parents looking for a new boarding school. I want to go back to my boarding school but if I want to go home I have to do what they say and tell me to do. I can't wait to get out of here. Sam is so weird. In the morning he just doesn't do anything then he transforms at night. I just don't get it.

Today Seeking Bow told me all about Clare. Apparently she pretended to her home town that she had cancer just to get attention. And she crapped herself so she had to wear his boxers. I was so surprised I felt a bit sick.

## DAY SEVENTEEN

Today we hiked eight miles. Clare deathmarched (where the group has to follow the slowest person) us because of her leg but I thought she did really well. We had a staff change today and we have 4 new staff: Crimson Moon, Jessica, Laurie and Elk of Tall Waters. They all seem really cool (so far). I will miss Seeking Bow.

We didn't do a full body (wash) *today so I smell! But I guess everyone else does too. I heard that Chris is doing well in the Eagles and Melissa still believes she might be pulled* (taken out of the programme). *I miss them both a lot and wish we were all in the same group but I'm happy I'm in the Firehawks because they are a cool group.*

**Goals:**
*Don't be nosey*
*Get a fire*

### DAY EIGHTEEN

*Today we hiked 5 miles. I think I did really well and I didn't deathmarch for once. I only wish it wasn't so hot. I also worked on fires today on our breaks and I got black punk and smoke. I can't wait till I get another fire because then I will be another step closer to going home.*

*I was right the new staff are really cool so it should be a good week. I saw Chris from the Eagles today. Apparently he's doing good and he looks like he's OK. Melissa has moved groups and Sam probably replaced her because he was put into the Eagles yesterday. So I had a good day today and I'm proud of my hiking.*

## DAY NINETEEN

*Today we walked 2 miles..........only joking. We hiked 15 miles! With our packs that weigh 50 lbs! That means we all got Gatorade!* (A fruit-flavoured power drink used by sports enthusiasts.) *That was a big achievement for me. It was really, really hard but I kept going and I got there in the end. My knees and legs felt like jelly but I didn't get that tired but in the end when we got to camp I could hardly walk! My feet still hurt.*

*Louise got taken to do her solo* (spending 24 hours on her own in the desert and reflecting on everything) *then we couldn't get a fire and it was pouring with rain and it was sooo cold. All in all I've had a good day but nobody can know we had to use a lighter for the fire to cook our supper!!!*

## DAY TWENTY

*Today was a cool day. We woke up and it was raining again. That sucked but we got a wiggi (lie in in our sleeping bags) morning. When we got up we went to get water. My blisters were really hurting and I was really stiff from the Gatorade hike yesterday. But I'm really proud of myself.*

*We did full body* (wash) *and got drop* (food supplies and

post) *for the first time on time since I came here! There were no letters from my mum again for the third week. I don't know why she isn't replying to any of my letters but I'm getting really upset about it.*

*We got two new 'wogs'* (Polliwogs, new students) *today. They are really cool and Will reminds me of Will Holyoake at home! Louise is doing well on her solo. I'm eating cold because I did not get a fire and I didn't try hard enough.*

## COOMBE HILL

Today I went to collect Tom from school for his half term holiday. Jonathan and I have agreed that he should have Tom every second weekend and so I will bring him home, wait for Jonathan to get down from Manchester and then I am off to stay at a girlfriend's house while she and her family are away sailing in Seaview. I feel deeply resentful that I have to clear out of my own home so that Jonathan can be there, but he says that it is his home too and he has every right to be there. I could argue, but I don't. Instead I spend a miserable couple of days all by myself in a strange house, writing to Emily and reading and not being able to sleep for thinking.

On the Bank Holiday Monday I went to my brother's and he and Liz took me out for lunch. It was a beautiful day and I had a nice time with them. I am aware that they may feel uncomfortable about my split with Jonathan – they have known him for twenty years after all – but they seem very supportive of what I am doing right now and are very loving. I have not told them that I think this may now be a permanent split, although it is on my mind much of the time. How can I even consider going back into the relationship? I feel that all we had together has been ruined over the last few months.

### DAY TWENTY-ONE

*Today we had a bit of a lay over day. Louise was still doing solo so we all worked on fires. I got black punk and smoke but no coal I'm afraid. Today Mark was really getting at me. Everything I did he had something to say about it. He really gets me all tense and stressed the way he always has something negative to say. I mean he can be really nice sometimes and he is a good singer!*

*We hiked really well today, we hiked 'Smiles' (the local name for a mountain) and Clare did really well. It was a really fun hike and I got to know the new 'wogs' a little more. We lost Elk today. He swapped with Nate. He seems cool and he is a reserve for the army which is awesome!*

*I'm finding this really hard. This morning we were talking about Avril Lavigne and it just reminded me of me and Daddy in the Porsche listening to her CD. I started crying and now all day I will be thinking of that because once I get a thought in my head it doesn't go away.*

*I'm so homesick it's unbelievable. I didn't realise I would miss you guys so much. And I will never ever do anything like this again because I don't want to end up like this in this place again.*

### DAY TWENTY-TWO

*Today was a really good day. I GOT MY SECOND FIRE!!!!!! Clare says she was working hard but she really didn't work or put any effort in. I think I worked pretty well and I'm glad that now I have realised when you actually work hard you get the best result. And you get the best feeling when you get a fire. It's a real natural high!*

*I'm getting on well here now and I'm getting used to waking up early! Even though I'm grumpy. Mark and I got on a lot better I think today. He helped me with my fire and we worked as a team which is good. I asked Doc Chris* (the therapist) *if she could ask my dad if he could let my boyfriend send me a letter. I hope he says yes.*

### Goals:
*Hand in Phases 2 and 3 tomorrow*
*Try harder with Mark*

## DAY TWENTY-THREE

*TODAY LOUISE GOT NAMED!!!!!!!!!*

(The whole process of 'naming' is based on the Native American Indian idea of giving a person a name, which best describes who they are and what they bring to the tribe. A strong boy with leadership qualities might, for instance, earn the name of 'Running Bull'. The naming ceremony is a powerful and emotional occasion where the whole tribe assembles and the Chief conducts an explanation of how the name has been earned. This is followed by the burning of sage brush around the outline of the person being named (cutting out the 'old' person) and then an invitation to step forward into their' new' role in the tribe. These ceremonies are carried out with great precision, and are considered as the highest honour by members of the tribe. So it is within the 'tribe' of Redcliff Ascent. Being 'named' is the highest accolade within the groups and those who earn 'names' are held in great esteem. Many of the group leaders have earned names and each person on the programme works towards being named, as the ultimate sign of personal regard in the 'tribe'. Generally, it is an accolade bestowed on people in the programme who are ready to leave or who have shown particular strength and bravery. Most of the 'names' mentioned here belong to staff or students about to graduate).

*Seeking Bow came with Crystal Fox to do the naming*

ceremony. When we were sitting down for dinner Crimson Moon took us for a walk. We saw Crystal Fox and she led Louise to a tree. Seeking Bow was up in the tree and Louise had to climb it. It was so pleasing seeing her being named. She looked so happy!

This morning we hiked 'Smiles' and got to camp at 1.30 at night!

## DAY TWENTY-FOUR

Today I gave in Phase 2. I hope I passed. I also made a necklace out of Ghost beads. The highlight of the day was realising that Crimson Moon looks like Winnie the Pooh! But I will not mention this again.

**Goals:**
I will not argue with staff

## DAY TWENTY-FIVE

I had the coolest day today. We had wiggi Wednesday (a lie in) which was awesome. We got up and hiked 2 miles to the bottom of a huge hill and took off our packs. We then hiked without our packs to the top of the hill and it was so high we could see everything. Mark got named on top of the cliff top, which was awesome. He got named 'Roaring Bull Hunting' which I think really suits him.

When we got to the water source we were sooo hot. I saw Reese for the first time since Polliwogs. He is on Phases 6 and 7 and he has his knife and back pack. He has done so well.

When we were getting water Crimson Moon let us go for a swim in the lake! So all us girls just jumped in the lake and came out after a long refreshing swim stinking of crap! I also saw Melissa. She's in the Bullfrogs (a group for those who have broken promises or have got themselves into serious trouble in the programme – a punishment group) with Ellie. Amanda was also put in the Bullfrogs for not behaving. I had an awesome day.

## DAY TWENTY-SIX

I had a really good day man! We woke up later than usual which was really, really awesome! We did a day hike and it was extremely hot and I was really hungry so I felt really sick and we climbed a steep hill and I was so scared because I am afraid of heights so I was shaking and crying. But I did it so I'm proud.

When we got to the top we went to the edge of the cliff and I *thanked my mum and dad for everything they did and I thanked everyone that tried so hard to help me, including Jun, my boyfriend, for helping me through hard times and being there for me every step of the way. I miss him.*

**Goals:**
*Be positive*
*Argue less*

### DAY TWENTY-SEVEN

*Today was a really good day. We woke up and we saw Golden Lion! He just randomly came into our campsite. Apparently, according to Clare, Golden Lion drove his 'burban'* (suburban truck) *right through our campsite in the middle of the night! He is such a cool guy. Anyway Connor is so annoying and rude to everyone. He is really thick too!*

*I wrote a letter back to my mum and my boyfriend. I explained to my mum what actually happened that night way back before I left home. It was hard to talk about it with Doc Chris but I do need to sort it out. I hate it soooooo much and I don't want to remember it!!*

*Burning the spice bag?* (dropped into the fire by mistake)
*Wow what a shame*

*A week without spices*
*Who's to blame?*

### DAYS TWENTY-EIGHT TO FIFTY-ONE ARE MISSING

It is extremely difficult to put together what was going on at this time. Our weekly conferences with the therapist were hugely frustrating, as Jonathan was still often struggling against airline announcements in the background as we talked to Utah via a radio set. The therapist's reports of Emily's progress seemed to contradict the weekly letters I received which increasingly portrayed a girl who was seriously upset and breaking down. Often I felt that the therapist's analysis lacked depth and intuition, as she raised issues that I believed were wide of the mark. Jonathan and I were constantly tempted into blaming each other for how Emily felt about herself, although we both tried very hard to be grown up about it.

Friends and family all called regularly for updates on Emily's progress and while I tried to be positive, I was beginning to cave in. I screened each and every letter I received for signs of her moving forward, but could not find many.

Now, sitting looking at her journals of this time, stuck together, ink running to illegible, dog-eared and decomposing with the damp, I wonder if Emily deliberately destroyed these pages. She says she can't remember anything about this time and that she fell into a river during a hike which destroyed her book. I don't know.

# Chapter 17

★ ☆ ★

**PHASE FIVE**

Northward is where winter dwells, it is a place where there are hardships and suffering, yet there is also a serene beauty. The northern lights crackle in the night as if the sky was on fire and the quietude of the white boreal forest has inspired countless poets through the years. So the north is where we turn to when we need strength or silence in our lives. The value of the north is honesty, it is here because it takes much strength of character to be honest, not only with others but, more importantly, with ourselves. This is a lifetime process and something that everybody works on. The colour of the north is white, like the canvas where everything is clean in preparation for a masterpiece. Like the winter that clears away all of the old in preparation for the newness of spring. White is a purifying colour and represents limitless potential. It also stands for the white races of humans. The totem of the north is Buffalo, at one time the American plains were blackened by mighty herds of bison. The buffalo find their strength in family and belonging, they present a united front to the world and so live without fear. They were the life of the plains tribes and, as the bison were decimated and scattered, so too were the native peoples of the west. Skills learned in this phase are; water; finding, treatment and usage, use of a modern back pack, more knots, bone tools and basic astronomy.

*Here is a poem written by my friend Erin who was with me in the
Firehawks for a while.*

**Emily**

*Your spirit flies in the wind*
*Your smile brings out the sun*
*Your laugh makes my day*
*Your personality sparkles and shines*
*Your attitude is contagious and*
*Your beauty makes life worth living*
*You are kind and unique*
*Even when the rain comes*
*You don't let it faze you*
*For you are beautiful*
*And should remember*
*How you affect other people*
*Like cold and heat*
*You are stunning and unexpected*
*You are a night bird inviting*
*Others to come play*

## COOMBE HILL

While Emily continued her journey in Utah, I was also continuing
my journey. By early June things were beginning to feel a little
different. I found my energy returning and I no longer felt wiped
out all the time. Life at home was calm. I was spending a lot of

time dog-walking with Harry and his friend Bolly Basset, whose owner, my friend Philippa, was very ill and unable to walk her. We went on long hikes, which provided me with some good thinking time. I was also delving into all sorts of books in an effort to try to get to grips with how and why things had gone so wrong with Emily, and with my marriage.

I started to develop some rules to govern my own thinking. I resolved to stop allowing Emily and Jonathan to invade my thoughts at any time of the day or night, so I disciplined myself to have periods of time when I banished them and thought about other things. This took a lot of determination because just receiving a letter from Emily, or a phone call from Jonathan, could upset my whole day and take me on a downwards spiral. Gradually, though, I started to improve at it and was much happier as a result.

I was, in fact, genuinely surprised to discover that I was not missing Jonathan, and was very much enjoying spending time with myself. I did arrange to see friends, and had some wonderful nights out, but I no longer needed to do this as an escape or a way of forgetting. I was more than happy curling up with the dog and a book – and not always a self-help book. I was really enjoying reading again as a form of relaxation.

I made sure that I kept some structure to my day, as my chaotic existence with Emily has taught me that I need that in my life.

But I also enjoyed breaking the rules sometimes, even going back to bed in the morning if I felt exhausted. This happened less and less as I started to eat properly and to exercise again. The long dark nights, previously so often ravaged by depression, hopelessness and anger, became fewer and fewer, and I really began to feel that I had regained control over myself.

My future with Jonathan was obviously a pressing problem and I think we were both putting in a lot of effort to sort ourselves out, although not together, since he was in Manchester, I was in London, and I was avoiding him when he came down for his weekends with Tom. I was continuing with counselling and he was seeing someone who was originally his work coach. Jonathan asked if I would see the same chap in the hope that, in knowing us both, he might be able to help us.

Initially I was reluctant. With my background in psychology, I am more comfortable with psychologists who are therapists, rather than management coaches whom I associate with dealing with work skills rather than personal skills. I was also hesitant about how I would accept someone who was an advocate for Jonathan, rather than for me. However, I did feel I owed it to him to try everything possible to save our marriage and so I agreed to go with an open mind.

I saw the coach several times during June. The programme was designed to allow for reflection on personal and family history in order to help understand the people and situations which have shaped you, and see your formative experience from another viewpoint. Making you aware of the factors that are driving you should enable you to see clearly, and take control in any situation, and make better and more informed choices.

The whole process was extremely valuable in that it crystallised a lot of where my thinking had been taking me, bringing together elements of the many books I have read, and providing some sort of logical explanation as to how we had got to where we were. I also got a sharp glimpse of things from Jonathan's viewpoint and began to understand how we both felt we were playing 'piggy in the middle' within our triangular relationship with Emily. It also became clear how, as long as four years ago, he had sought help for his anger problems when they spilled over into his work situation.

The truth that emerged from these sessions is not very palatable. I had become a co-dependent to both Emily and Jonathan. While I was thinking that I was being extremely caring and supportive as a wife to Jonathan, and as a mother to Emily (who, after all, has many difficulties to face due to her ADHD) I was actually enabling them to be difficult people. I constantly rescued Emily from difficult situations, I sat on my own anger in order to appear calm and understanding during her tantrums, I kept her in school by negotiating with her teachers and, unwittingly of course, was making it possible for her to continue with her self-destructive behaviour.

In my quest for love, to be needed and highly regarded, I played the chameleon, taking my colours from my surroundings, a people pleaser, never able to say 'No' and seemingly self-sacrificing. But beneath the apparent saintliness I was actually seeking to control them both. (I recognised the 'control' issue – the more out of control Emily became, the more I felt drawn into controlling her). Co-dependents are the world's supreme 'looker-afterers', the copers, eternal optimists who always know that better days are just ahead. They tell you that things are 'not so bad', that 'it's getting better' – even when it is obvious that their world is crashing about their ears. Apparently, co-dependents do not have a strong personal sense of identity and possess little sense of self-worth, they over-identify with their roles and relationships. Instead of being a woman who also is a mother, a co-dependent woman will see herself first and foremost as a 'mother'.

Co-dependents are also compulsive in everything they do. They may be compulsive workaholics or drinkers, overachievers (me for sure). If you are severely co-dependent, it will eventually lead to illness and continuous, unrelenting depression. These people become ill because, however hard they try, however self-sacrificing, high-achieving or workaholic they may be, they never gain any sense of satisfaction, never know when to stop. Also, inwardly, co-dependents are full of rage, anger, hostility and resentment towards people who don't appreciate them enough; they feel exploited and this can cause great stress, which is responsible for many physical, mental and emotional illnesses.

Too much of this felt familiar but, since it is essentially learned behaviour, all I would have to do is unlearn it! Under the guidance of the coach, I worked on creating my own personal development plan.

## MY ACTION PLAN FOR THE FUTURE OF OUR FAMILY

I need to rediscover myself as distinct from my roles as mother and wife. What will help me to do this is to re-engage with my postgraduate course in Psychology. I need to qualify and then find a job through which I will achieve validation for my intellectual strengths and social skills.

I must put in place a series of boundaries, which I can use to protect my need for space to study and to work; to have defined time that I can devote to the children; and, in the longer term, to have time which can be for Jonathan. I must not let Jonathan take over time set aside for other things. Because I am so accustomed to letting Jonathan and the children eat up my time and then use the left-over time for my studies (which has put a lot of extra pressure on me), and these habits become entrenched, I need to do this in stages. I need to start by coping with the children – giving them my time during their school holidays, and then start back with my studies in September. Because Jonathan 'steals' my time from them and my work, I need to have more time when I do not need to consider his day-to-day needs and mood swings. As both children are at boarding school, this will help me to keep the boundaries between them and having a life of my own. If Emily is unable to stay in her school I must then be sure not to put down the rest of my life for her. It was a mistake to do this before and I am now certain that it would not work for either of us if I were to do it again.

In terms of boundaries, I need to set limits on what I can be expected to do for Emily. She is now nearly 15 and I need to let go of her. She must take her own path in life and I must stop trying to rescue her or trying to catch her before she falls.

I must let Jonathan stand on his own two feet. This means I need to stop worrying if he will lose his job; stop apologising for him when he is rude to people or is late; stop trying to justify his behaviour to friends, family and the children; stop hoping that he will be strong, and accept that he is not.

As a mother I must raise my expectations of what the children should be contributing at home. They must take some responsibility for some of the chores and they must do things for me sometimes.

In order for the children to get a period of special time with me, I must find something I can share with each of them and make time to do it. We all need to accept that we are not a family that can expect to play happily together, so look for things that we can do in twos. Then Emily will not feel such an outcast (she never wants to join in) and Tom will not feel under pressure to 'do' things all the time. I need to plan things with each child so that they are doing what they want to but including me.

The kids and I always used to enjoy our time together in the Isle of Wight – the only one who did not enjoy it was Jonathan. We must agree that nobody expects him to come and that is time for me with the children on our own. I must also encourage Jonathan to have an equivalent time with them, and without me, so they can have their special times together too.

The main critical success factor will be that I will continue to feel energised, rather than wiped out, stressed, and unwilling to face the day. I will also begin to have a focus in my life that is outside the family and not dependent on how things are going with the children or with Jonathan.

I must also decide if our marriage can continue and be honest about how I feel towards Jonathan. Not just hang on in there for the sake of the children and because I am scared he will fall apart if we split. I need to be frank and honest with him about when I am unhappy and what has caused it, instead of relying on hopes of 'getting through this rough patch' all the time. Then I will have less reason to be resentful that he doesn't understand how I feel.

Instead of giving in to Jonathan when he bullies us all, I must learn to stand firm and to say 'No' and, when necessary, say 'No' on behalf of the children. In this way I will show the children, Emily in particular, that it is necessary to learn when to say 'No' and that it is OK to disagree, even when it makes the other person angry. If I am strong then Emily will learn that it is OK for women to be strong – we don't have to give in all the time.

I must stop allowing Jonathan to be the 'good parent' and thereby forcing me to be the 'bad parent'. Throughout our separation I need to ensure that the children can see that I can be both types of parent on my own, rather than letting Jonathan come home and either not be strong enough to discipline them, or overriding decisions made by me in his absence.

All of this will take a lot of practice and I notice that as soon as Jonathan is back in the house we revert to our old ways. I am scared that our separation will be meaningless unless we can make some real changes. If we don't, that will be the end of our relationship, as I will not go back to how things were.

For this reason, I want Emily to come home to us as separate people and to rebuild her relationships with us initially as individuals, not as a couple. We will need to go very slowly with her. She is bound to make mistakes as she tries out her new life and makes it fit her. I want to establish some very firm boundaries in behaviour and attitude and I don't want her to be able to play Jonathan off against me or allow Jonathan to play me off against Emily.

I am so weary of being the strong one, of having to deal with whatever life throws at us, and of having to take the lead in keeping things together. I feel that Jonathan, Emily and Tom expect me to be the peacemaker in the family, that I constantly have to be alert to potential conflicts and act to divert them. Yet when I fail it is somehow my fault. It always seems unacceptable for me to throw a tantrum and yet everyone else is allowed to. This all gives me a feeling of having to hold myself in, watching what I say all the time. It's like walking on eggshells with Jonathan, and with Emily in particular. I feel I am never able to relax and be myself.

In spite of going through this process, I am really not certain if Jonathan and I have a future together. I am worried that too much has happened and I feel a great gulf between us at the moment. I am no longer sure of my true feelings for him as I still feel quite overwhelmed with anger and resentment. I am not prepared to simply 'give it another try' – I have done that many times already. I feel that I need more time – I must have time with Emily by ourselves too. If Jonathan pushes for an answer then at the moment I just don't feel I can make an honest commitment to our future together. I know that means repeating the family history of broken families, but it might mean that Emily and Tom won't have to.

### DAY FIFTY-TWO

*Today I woke up and after breakfast we had to roll up our packs and do camp chores which all took so long. We missed all our free time so far this week, which is really bad, and it sucks. We tried to bring this group together more and all work together much more as a team. We are the Firehawks. The best group in the field and we need to live up to that. I spoke to Rain Raven and he said I was a leader in this group and I need to stop being like this and start leading the group on towards a positive outlook on this programme. I know we can all do it.*

*Onwards towards a distant plain*
*Onwards towards the deep red sunset*
*Onwards towards life*
*Over the hills*
*Striding and sweating*
*It feels so good thinking and wondering*
*Tomorrow we will rise again*
*Onwards, onwards*

**Goals:**

Lead the group positively

Don't get too frustrated and take it out on the group

## *DAY FIFTY-THREE*

Today was an OK day. Joe had got no sleep last night and had really bad sunburn and had got his crap all on his pants. He was boiling them when we got up and he was not feeling very good. I felt really sorry for him because he then had to do the hike and he was soooo tired. I hope he feels better. I tried to be a better leader today and I don't know if my efforts worked but I hope it did.

*Shindig* (when groups all come together for a party) *is two days away and we all can't wait to eat good food. My birthday is in one week now and I can't wait to turn 15. I have already been sent birthday cards, which is cool, but I did want to be home for it.*

The fire burns with extreme beauty

Dancing to and fro

Burning with delight

Smoke billows out from the tips of the flames

Wandering and weaving through the darkness

**Goals:**

*Be a successful leader*
*Turn in Phase 6*

## COOMBE HILL

Alan came to start redecorating the house. While he gradually moved around from room to room, I was forced to clear each space before he was able to begin. This caught me up in a frenzy of clearing out cupboards and re-evaluating our possessions that occupied me for many days. I went through every nook and cranny in the house, getting rid of sacks of things long-forgotten or outgrown, tidying, reorganising furniture. I was possessed with a need to renew our home, to make it clean and beautiful, a sort of 'refeathering' of the nest. It felt great. The house, long-neglected, became once more the home that Jonathan and I had so lovingly and painstakingly put together. The whole process was immensely satisfying and I felt good about everything.

## *DAY FIFTY-FOUR*

*We hiked four miles from Mountain Springs to Deadmans today. It was my first hike with my pack and my hips were killing me. I swear I'm going to get a bruise from where my pack was. Joe hiked really fast and only stopped for one break but it was OK because we weren't hiking up and down loads of hills. When we got to camp we set up in 45 minutes. We then had a lot of time to do phase work which was awesome!*

*Will bust a coal and got the group fire tonight which I thought was rad* (radical) *of him. The water source we are using is Culver Springs and it is ages away. I hope Erin gets a fire. She really does deserve to go home.*

## *DAY FIFTY-FIVE*

*Today was an alright day. I had therapy and I spoke to Doc Chris about what was going on at home. Apparently she spoke to my mum about what is happening between her and my dad. My mum is taking time to think things over and if they could rebuild the relationship or not. I hope my mum can forgive my dad for what he did. He loves us too much.*

## *DAY FIFTY-SIX*

*Today was the coolest day. We got up and we spent two hours looking for water. When we were going back to our camp we saw the Eagles. Chris was there and he told me that he hadn't forgotten me. We also saw Danielle and she yelled 'Buff Babe' to Connor! She fancies him! We hiked to Outpost and Jesse fell and hurt his ankle so we all had to wait while he sat there for a while crying. Then he deathmarched us the rest of the way.*

*I think we did good on our song and dance and I hope we win! Amanda and I have a something for Joe tonight. I hope he likes the surprise.*

*Shindig was the best thing that has ever happened to me! It was soooo fun. Liz is now in our group. She is cool and she made Firedrum cry! Ha ha!*

*The day was awesome until I got caught sending my address to Chris. He gave me his and Tres said I could keep it which was awesome of him but then Nash saw me looking at it so he took it. I'm soooo upset about Chris and also about Joe leaving to graduate. I want him back.*

**Goals:**
*Be a positive leader*
*Don't get frustrated so easily*

### DAY FIFTY-SEVEN

*Today was an awesome day. Our staff are so cool. I gave Chris my address and I read his song this morning and it's so good. We went to get water and we walked together and he showed me his bruises and we started kissing. HE'S SO FIT. HE'S SO FUCKING HOT. Hopefully he is joining us for dinner tonight.*

*We hiked miles today. It was fun.*

*I love my food and my tum tum*

**Goals:**

*Be good*

*Be positive*

### DAY FIFTY-EIGHT

*Today was cool. Liz got moved groups which was really sad. I really liked Liz. She liked all the songs I liked and we were singing them all night. Best night. She was awesome. I woke up this morning and I missed my mum (AND CHRIS). I can't wait till I graduate so I can see my parents and when I go back to LA I can hook up with Chris.*

*The new guy Adam is cool. He's really nice and I'm glad he doesn't deathmarch like most other 'wogs'. I like talking to him about my boyfriend and his girlfriend.*

**Goals:**

*What we talked about today!*

# Chapter 18

## PHASE SIX

In this phase the direction is down, or the earth. In most 'primitive' cultures, the people believed that the earth was their mother. That in a sense we actually belong to the earth. In modern society it is believed that the earth belongs to us (that may explain the bad way in which we treat it). It is from the earth that we receive nourishment and a place to walk and sleep. Our bodies are made up of the same stuff as the earth and it is back to the earth that they will go when we die. The value of Phase six is work, an apt choice, it is by work that we live, by the sweat of our brows do we earn our bread. Maybe because we are punished so much with work when we are growing up, we learn to dislike physical labour as adults. Yet there is much honour and joy in work. The colour of this direction is brown, strong and rich, the basis from which all life springs. It also represents the brown races of humans. The totem of the earth is Badger, who is a hard worker, a good provider and so fierce that most other animals leave them alone. Yet for all of that they are nurturing parents and very intelligent. Skills learned in this phase are; compass use, traps and snares, tracking and more tool making.

*Dear Mum*
*I'm so pissed off at the moment. I'm going to be here for ever now because I can't do my stupid traps* (designed to

catch small animals for food). *I couldn't give in any phases last week and I'm not going to be able to graduate in two weeks now because if I don't turn in Phase 6 this week then I can't turn in Phases 7 and 8 next week. I'm so angry at everything and everyone because all the staff are annoying me and taking the piss out of the notches on the trap pieces that I have made. It's fucking me right off!*

## DAY FIFTY-NINE

*Today was so frustrating. I HATE TRAPS. THEY ARE SOOOO FRIGIN ANNOYING !!!!!! I was so pissed off with everything today and I know I shouldn't be because my goal is to be leader and it's bad that I'm being negative again.*

*Me and Erin had fun today, laughing and writing stuff to each other.*

*Connor was annoying us. He acts so dumb and he just pisses everyone off. Amanda's being cool today (I think she has a crush!) Anyway we laid over which was awesome except I didn't get my traps done.*

## DAY SIXTY 4<sup>th</sup> July

*Today was an awesome day! We got up early and hiked to J B Mine. Last week we night hiked there. It was a good hike* but my pack was really hurting me. Me and Amanda were having fun today. WE WENT SWIMMING but it was so cold. We saw Earth Warrior and Climbing Bear and Melissa. I hope she's doing well.

I'm so tired
I wanna eat
I'm so frustrated
And very beat.

**Goals:**
To get less frustrated
To not fight with Connor and just ignore him
Change my attitude
Spend less time crying and talking

### DAY SIXTY-ONE
Today was a crap day. I was in such a bad mood from the moment I got up. I was really pissed because my traps did not work and I was getting frustrated. We hiked 6.5 miles and my hips were killing me. I swear I'm going to drop this pack.

I named Nash today. I named him Sunrise Badger.

We all raced the Bullfrogs and Earth Warrior to our camps but they won because they are such big heads!

## DAY SIXTY-TWO

*Dear Mummy*

*I'm so upset. My birthday has been the crappiest day of my life.*

*I was supposed to hand in Phases 6 and 7 this week but I can't because of my traps. Also it's a tradition here to give two boxes of cup cakes to a student when it's their birthday but of course my staff think I don't deserve them.*

*I HATE MYSELF I HATE MYSELF I HATE MYSELF I HATE MYSELF I HATE MYSELF*
*I WANT TO DIE I WANT TO DIE I WANT TO DIE I WANT TO DIE I WANT TO DIE*
*DEPRESSION*
*I HATE HURTING I HATE HURTING I HATE HURTING I HATE HURTING*

This goes on for page after page with cutting and tearing and then:

*Today was my birthday. I can't believe I hiked 20 miles.*

*Winter Raven came this morning to give my hat back and he made me do a war dance and then he made me hike with him. He's really cool.*

*Connor bust his hand today punching a tree. There was blood everywhere. He's in the hospital.*

*I missed my mum so much today. I wanna go home. I know all I need to do is get my traps. Erin got her fires and graduated. I'm really pleased for her but I wished it was me at grad*

*Depression, hatred*
*Hurting, upsetting*
*Cutting, slitting*
*Silence*

## COOMBE HILL

Emily's fifteenth birthday – and she is not here. I can hardly bear it. I was so certain that she would be out of the programme by now but she shows no signs of finishing. She is fighting everyone and everything and I know from her therapist that she is in emotional turmoil. I will never understand why, with everyone on her side, she continues to oppose everybody. What is going on inside that little head of hers? I am worried that the staff at Redcliff cannot deal with her. What if she does something like cutting herself again? Oh my God, this is all too much to bear.

### DAY SIXTY-THREE

**Things I like:**
Spirit Fox playing guitar
My pack
My knife
Phase meals
Rain Raven
Letters
My birthday
Phases
Gifts people made for me

**Autobiography 6:**

I have only ever lived in one place out of the UK. That would be in the US in Washington, DC. We went to live there from Hammersmith in London because my dad's work moved. After we spent a couple of years in Washington we came back to London to live in Kingston. I have been to many places before and I have been very lucky to travel as I have.

I remember one of my favourite holidays was when I went to the south of France with my best friend, Olivia, her two older brothers, another family and of course their parents. Their parents are really awesome so we got to do loads of things! We had a villa on the beach with little stone steps leading down to the sea. It was so hot so none of us could get to sleep at night so most nights we would all stay out till about three in the morning and then go back to our villa and swim in our pool.

It was such a great holiday and the Simpsons are like my second family.

Another good holiday was when we went to Cuba. We got off the plane and went to our hotel which was a 5 star hotel right on the beach. We arrived at the hotel and found out that they didn't have our rooms! So we got driven to another hotel down the beach. It was a wonderful holiday and we all really enjoyed it by the beach. We were at our beach hotel for a week and a half then we flew to Havana and stayed there for a week. It was an overall great holiday.

I have also been abroad to Los Angeles, Florida, Switzerland, France, Belgium and basically all the European countries. I love vacations.

**Ten Lifetime Goals:** (but of course, being Emily, there are only six!)

1. Become a therapist – study a lot at college and complete my courses.

2. *Get over my phobias of fish and heights. Challenge myself by climbing and swimming in the sea.*
3. *Travel round the world – earn some money in some way ie. Get a job for travel expenses.*
4. *Climb Mount Everest – raise money for it and do it for charity.*
5. *Become a ski racer – train really hard and keep skiing for the British Ski Academy.*
6. *Finish this programme.*

## DAY SIXTY-FOUR: SAGE GROUSE

*Today was a good day. We got no sleep last night because the shelter was falling apart and flapping. It was too windy! Clare had to sleep on top of the tarp so it wouldn't fly undone! It pissed me off because I was also sleeping on freaking rocks!*

*We slept in today which was awesome and Connor went off to get his cast on for his hand. Clare went to Redhands this week. I know this sounds mean but we are all thankful she has gone! We deathmarched today for 5 miles and it really, really sucked. Matt fell over like three times. I remember the time when Jesse pretended to break his ankle and no one cared! Ha, ha, ha. Matt is also scared of the dark so he couldn't collect wood on his own.*

**Goals:**

Positively motivate people in my group
Don't give up


## DAY SIXTY-FIVE: SAGE GROUSE (TRACTOR SPRINGS)

Today has been a good day so far! I DID MY TRAPS!!!

Finally I got all my traps signed off! I'm so pleased because now I can turn in three phases this week and be eligible for the next Graduation! YAY! I can hopefully go home! I pray that I will pass all my BYUs (assignments). After two and a half weeks of trying and then giving up I made my goal!

I can't wait to hike tonight. I don't know why. Actually I do. It's drop tomorrow so I can hopefully go on solo quicker if we get there sooner but then we have MATT to think about.

Nobody likes the poor kid. Conner had to pick up all his stuff for him which really pissed him off! We are all having a hard time coping with him.

**Goals:**

Finish all phase work and start on BYUs
Go on solo

# Chapter 19

**PHASE SEVEN**

The next direction is up, or the sky. If the earth is our floor, the sky is our ceiling, here is light and air and rain and wind. The sun, rainbows and clouds. Many cultures believed, and still believe in a 'sky country' or heaven. The value of this direction is trust, to trust is to have faith in something or someone. Like many other values we find that we have to find faith in ourselves before we can find it in others. The colour of the sky is blue, blue is cool and soothing, it is a royal colour and represents devotion to principles. The totem of this direction is Eagle. Eagle soars high and travels far, he sees things far off and dreams big. Yet he also knows the importance of starting small. Skills learned in this phase are; topographical maps, primitive lighting, goal setting and a 48-hour solo experience.

### *DAY SEVENTY: LOWER TETONS*

*Today was soooo crap. The little rat was sitting and crying and wailing. I hate him. He's so stupid. Nobody likes him. We were hiking for two minutes and he sat!!! So we had to walk while North River Laughing shouted at him and stuff. At the end of the hike he came up to us and said 'that was a good hike'. WHAT THE CRAP!*

*We also have a new 'wog' (another one!!! Base hates us!!) His name is Marc. He's really weird and he doesn't sit or talk to any of us. I haven't eaten for like 24 hours because of how long it's been taking us to hike. I'm so starving.*

## DAY SEVENTY-ONE: LOWER TETONS

*Today was a good day! I gave in Phases 6 and 7 and passed both of them. I won't graduate this grad but I will next grad because I'm giving in Phase 8 next week so I'll be done with my phases and I'll be able to call out hemp and beads finally. Matt is still frigging annoying us all.*

*Doc Chris spoke to my mum and she has been inviting my boyfriend round to our house. She wants to chat to him more. She said there's another letter on its way from him so hopefully I'll get it tomorrow at staff change. Will made me a bracelet today. It's really pretty.*

### Introspection:

*If you say to yourself that you are not going to win something that you are doing you are not going to win it and you won't succeed at whatever it is. Whereas if you say to yourself 'Yes, I'm going to do this and I'm going to succeed in every way possible' and you try your hardest then you will do it.*

*Autobiography 7:*

*People have betrayed my trust.*

*My little brother knew of the things I was doing behind my parents' back. Whenever they went out I'd throw parties or go out when I was actually supposed to be babysitting him. At the end of the night I'd tell him not to tell mum and dad and he said he wouldn't. And he didn't until when we had fights he would go and tell my mum everything I had trusted him not to tell them so I'd get into trouble and he'd get back at me and he'd betray all the trust in me.*

*I'd also betray my parents' trust in many other ways. Whenever I was grounded in the house I'd try everything just to get out. I must have run away loads and loads of times and I always got into trouble with the police, which really betrayed my parents' trust in me.*

*I didn't trust my parents when they sent me here. I thought they were doing it to punish me for everything I've done but I then realised and have realised throughout this programme that they did it to help me.*

*I trust them and what they say now. My mum's been totally truthful about the situation between her and my dad and I trust them to help me and be there for me when I need them most.*

*Will and I wrote a poem for my mum*

**Mother and Daughter**

*Sealed with a kiss*
*Written with a heart*
*A mother and a daughter*
*Should never be apart*
*I hurt you in the past*
*But now it's time to heal*
*And I will give you love*
*And it shall be real*
*We will walk hand in hand*
*Down the path of life*
*Help each other all the way*
*Through our pains and our strife*
*For we have a love*
*Which cannot be broken*
*And feelings*
*Which cannot be spoken*

## COOMBE HILL

When this poem arrived in a letter I almost fell apart. After such a long time of feeling estranged from my daughter I felt this was evidence of a real change of heart. I cried every time I read it (which was often). I was so full of hope that she was at last turning a corner and would be back with us soon. Why I felt this so strongly I do not know. It would be totally unreasonable to expect, because she had written this tender note, that she had made a fundamental shift. I guess I just hoped so. I suppose I was clutching at straws.

## DAY SEVENTY-TWO

Today was a good day. We got up and (having wiggi Wednesday) went to get water. Iron Wolf told us to be really encouraging to Matt even though it's really hard because it could keep us back from graduating!

We had breakfast and Matt dumped out his whole pot on the ground and Noon found it and Matt blamed it all on me!!

We had staff change and got Climbing Bear, Alex, Lindsay and Calming Dove. We all circled up and Climbing Bear told us that we could do the Three Peaks hike!!! Matt told us all that he would try his hardest to do this. We then started hiking and Matt sat down within ten minutes of the hike and refused to go on. He then got up and hiked well but then sat again and was very rude to Calming Dove. We got to camp and ate our stovies (corned beef, beans and potato) *and went to sleep.*

**Goals:**
*Be less frustrated with Matt*
*Be positively motivating*

### DAY SEVENTY-THREE

*Today was a crap day. We can't do Three Peak because Matt sat down 6 times and at the end Climbing Bear said that if he did it one more time then we would turn back and hike for the rest of the week! So Matt sat down again!!!! He's such a selfish brat. Everyone is so totally pissed off at him and when Connor gets back he's going to freaking cut Matt's little ratty head off and stick it on a stick and carry it around sooo triumphantly. Anyway, Climbing Bear was really cool about it and so were Calming Dove and Alex.*

### DAY SEVENTY-FOUR: NORTH OBSERVATION

*I don't know how a person so small and ugly can upset me so much. We had such an awesome opportunity this week – to do Three Peak and Gatorade. First he messes up Three Peak for us and then the Gatorade hike. He says he cares about the group but he really doesn't at all. He's on separates (being apart from the group) still and I hope it stays like that.*

*Amanda is being really harsh to everyone at the moment. I don't think she realises that everyone has feelings and not just her.*

*I hope we get to zone by the end of the week. The Buffalos are already at Lone Pine!!! Oh well hopefully it will get better.*

## DAY SEVENTY-FIVE: JACKSON

*LA LA LA LA LA LA LA LA LA LA LA LA LA LA LA LA LA LA LA LA LA LA LA LA LA*

*Today was a rough day. We slept in and got up after hearing on the radio that the Buffalos are already at Butcher!! But we are not complaining because we finally got drop!!!! I CANT BELIEVE WE GOT PEANUT BUTTER!!!*
*Anyway, we had a day of whining and being so hot and pissed off with Matt. I don't want Amanda to leave tomorrow. I mean I will be really happy for her but I will also be really upset.*

**Goals:**
Deal with crap
Eat phase meals

## DAY SEVENTY-SIX: DEADMAN'S

Today was a really, really, really, really, really bad day. I am now number 1 in the group (I have been here the longest). Amanda has left and gone to graduate. I'm so upset and I can't stop crying when I think of her cute turtle face when she takes off her glasses. I miss her sooo much. She was great and we were best of friends after she came back from Bullfrogs. I will hopefully be allowed to visit her or meet up with her at Melrose or Magic Mountain in LA.

It rained so hard when we got to camp, which sucked and now we have to light a fire.

# Chapter 20

★ ✪ ★

## PHASE EIGHT

The last of the directions is inside of us, because it is necessary to internalise all of the lessons we have learned so far. Inside is where we live and feel and think, it is our true home, so it's important that it be comfortable for us. The value here is compassion, because it must come from inside. The colour is green, the colour of life. The totem of this direction is human. All of the animals have their attributes, some are fast, some are strong, some brave or clever. To some we ascribe nobleness of character of strength of heart and it is good to look for inspiration from our animal brothers and sisters. However, all of those things, speed, keenness of eye or claw, they come naturally to the animals. That is the way they were made, they don't have to work for it or think about it. An animal is incapable of going against its instinct of the natural order, they cannot 'sin'. Humans are the only beings that have the ability to go against nature and unfortunately we often do, the results being all too evident in the world around us. But what we do we can undo and though we are capable of the greatest wrongs, humans also possess the capacity to create the greatest beauty and right. Skills learned in this phase are; leadership, mentoring, orienteering, medicine shield (externalising internal existence) and gifting.

### DAY SEVENTY-SEVEN: DEADMAN'S

Today I had a very stressful day. It rained all over us last night and I was so soaked when I woke up! We hiked six miles to Deadmans and we passed Outpost. When we were hiking to the meadow water source we saw the Grad bus and all the parents!!!! It made me think to myself that I really should have given in Phase 8 last week when I had the chance and I could be grading with Amanda and my parents could have been on that bus coming to get me from Outpost. But oh well.....we have a new 'wog' in our group and she's from LONDON!! I'm so happy and she knows loads of gangs near where I live in Kingston. She likes rap, r 'n b and hip hop too!!

### DAY SEVENTY-EIGHT: MILL'S CREEK

Today I felt like crap and I couldn't get coals so I didn't give in Phase 8.

MATT'S IN BULLFROGS!!

We are all so relieved that little crap head has left our group. Now next week we can hopefully do Three Peak! I hope we get good staff next week so we can have a 'rad' week.

*I hope I will be able to graduate next time. If not I'm going to be very sad!!! I want to hike Bible tomorrow but we aren't.*

*Journals must be a page and a half*
*The other day I saw a calf*
*The rain sucks when you get wet*
*It feels good when you work up a sweat*
*Our pathetic friend is finally gone*
*We won't worry about waking at dawn*
*So let's eat our meal and go to bed*
*And not worry all week about crap head.*
          *By Climbing Bear*

### DAY SEVENTY-NINE: MILL'S CREEK

*Today was really cool. We had wiggi Wednesday which was cool but then Climbing Bear woke us up by pulling the tarp over our heads and screaming 'FIREHAWKS'!!!!! into our ears. Anyway, we all got up and ate breakfast then me and Climbing Bear had a water fight and he whacked me over the head with a freaking Nalgene!!!!!* (plastic container) *It was so funny but very painful.*

*I am now a Dog Soldier which is awesome. It means I get to go off for a week and do some community project. It is a real honour to be chosen. I've always wanted to work with*

*Redhawk and now I can. Also Ellie is with me. YAY! Everyone seems really, really nice so we should all have a 'rad' time. The food we have looks sooooo good!!*

## COOMBE HILL

FINALLY, FINALLY, on our weekly conference call to Emily's therapist it looks as if we can start to think about Emily graduating. We have been given the go-ahead to book flights in anticipation of her finishing on Monday 2nd August. I feel like I'm going to burst. I was so excited that Jonathan and I immediately began to make some plans. I hardly dared think of the days ahead – eleven days and she would be out. What would she be like? Certainly she looked a little different judging from the photographs we had been sent. I just couldn't wait.

After the initial euphoria had worn off a little, I began to feel anxious. What if the programme hadn't worked? What if she came back and got up to her old tricks again? Also, how would I manage going to the States with Jonathan to get her. It was compulsory that both birth parents attended the graduation and there would also be a parents' conference to go to where we would receive guidance on how to manage our children once we got them home. There was suddenly so much to consider and I must confess to another sleepless night. I just longed for this whole journey to be over. I wanted so much to just get on with our lives – I felt like we had been in some sort of hiatus for so long. So much thinking, analysing and soul searching. I was just desperate for us all to put these horrid years behind us and make a new start.

## DAY EIGHTY: DOG SOLDIERS – MILLS CREEK

*Today we got up really early and ate cold which sucked because we were all expecting pancakes and maple syrup. We got our boots on and hiked without our packs. We started work on a trail going up over a mountain so the cowboys could take their cattle up there. It was really hard work especially when it took 5 hours to hack a log in half! (At least it felt that long – we have no idea of real time out here – we have to guess from looking at the sun.)*

*Some of Redhawk's friends, the cowboys, came up the trail with their horses and gave us all Gatorade Then they dropped off bacon, steak, buffalo burgers, soda, coke, candy and loads of other things But we didn't get any today which sucks.*

## DAY EIGHTY-ONE: SUMMIT TRAIL

*Today was soo cool. We have the food at last. YAY! We cleared the rest of the trail up through the summit and we finished off in a beautiful valley. It's one of the most pretty things I have ever seen in my life. It was so magical and* breathtaking. We hiked all the way up our trail and it was something I wouldn't want to do over again. It was tiring but in the end it is good coz we have all this good grub.

RUB A DUB DUB
THANX 4 THE GRUB

### DAY EIGHTY-TWO: SUMMIT TRAIL, SECOND CUT

Today was a bad day. We got up and ate oats and fruit then we set up on the trail to go further and clear more trails. It started off OK but then got harder and more frustrating. I got sooooo frustrated and Noon was pissing me off so I stuck my middle finger up at him and walked off. He made me write a four page paper and pick up a rock. I guess I deserved it but it sucks anyway.

We are all sooooo hungry and we wanna eat goooooooood food. YAY!

**Goals:**
Manage frustration

### DAY EIGHTY-THREE: SUMMIT TRAIL

Today was a good day. Me and Ellie were collecting rocks to carry down to the water and it was really hard work. I *think we did really, really well. We are all soooooo tired from all the work and we are all soooo pleased that all our work is done. I can't wait to get back to my group and bust out four coals so I can be eligible to Grad. That would be cool. The cowboys came back today and brought us more sodas, candy and burritos etc...It's so exciting!!!*

*I'm so hungry*
*I wanna eat*
*I love cowboys*
*They bring good meat*

***Goals:***
*Get 4 coals*
*Graduate*

## COOMBE HILL

I went into overdrive making plans for the trip to bring Emily home. Jonathan was also planning the best way to get up to Utah and researching a special place in Arizona where we could all spend a few days together after her graduation. I made a series of elaborate plans to drive back from Arizona to Los Angeles to see Janette, Bob and everyone before returning to England.

I also had to think about Tom who, after careful consideration, we felt should not make this journey with us. Dear friends, Peter and Gillian, parents from his school, came up with a plan for him and their son to go off on a golf and tennis training camp in Sussex. Jonathan and Tom would then spend some time together on his return from the States.

After so long waiting for this moment, there was suddenly so much to organise. And the prospect of seeing Emily again was wonderful.

### DAY EIGHTY-SEVEN: COTTONWOOD CREEK

*Watsup Amy! It's great to be back in the group. I'm going to miss David, Danni, Vinnie and KT and Eleanor! Hopefully I will graduate with Papa Vinnie and Danni but everyone else is going home this coming Tuesday.*

*Dog Soldiers was so awesome. We got really good NORMAL food every meal and we got snacks. It's so weird to be back in the group!!!! But it's cool to be with everyone again. Joe is being cool. I did miss his farts and his stupid sarcastic jokes. We got awesome staff this week so hopeful it will be a good week.*

*Goals:*
*Manage frustration*
*Get 4 coals this week*

## COOMBE HILL

Jonathan was doing well with all the travel plans and confirmed our flights for Friday 30th July out to Phoenix, Arizona. We planned to overnight at a resort we had been to before in Sedona and then make the long drive up through the Sedona National Park, across the Painted Desert and on northwards to Utah. We would overnight in St George in order to arrive at the Redcliff Ascent base in Enterprise for 9.00 am Monday morning, in time for the parents' conference. Emily would graduate later that day.

I got packing. I packed for Tom's trip with his friend, I packed (and repacked several times) a suitcase for Emily (we had left her stuff in LA) and I organised for Harry, our Labrador, to go once more to Perry.

### *DAY EIGHTY-EIGHT: EAST GATE*

*Today was an OK day. I'm back on fire separates (where I am all on my own away from the group) which is the worst thing ever but the good thing is I got two coals. Now all I need is two more so I'm half way there. I will hopefully get them tomorrow so I can call out a book (someone who is putting in a lot of effort can request a book to read from the library back at base camp).*

*I miss my mum so much at the moment. I promised her I would graduate this grad. And because I was on Dog*

*Soldiers I didn't have time to get my coals. It really sucks. I've let everyone that was expecting me home down. I feel terrible.*

*It sucks to be no longer part of the group*
*To not join in the laughter and the fights*
*I need to get off separates soon*
*Or I will face doom!!!!*

**Goals:**
*Get coals*
*Manage frustration*

# Chapter 21

## COOMBE HILL

At some point in the evening Jonathan telephoned. He had received an urgent email from Redcliff. Emily would not be graduating. She hadn't completed her phase-work as expected and was not ready to leave the programme.

That night I went through a maelstrom of emotion. We had no further information and would have to wait until tomorrow to speak to Emily's therapist to find out exactly what had gone wrong. I couldn't believe this was really happening. There must be some mistake. Maybe she was holding back until the last moment and would surprise us all. It would be typical of her old behaviour to do such a thing.

I was incapable of doing anything. It would be an understatement to say I was upset. But I was also unreasonably angry. How could she do this to us? After all that we had been through. She had now been at Redcliff for 88 days! The average is 45-65 days. It was costing us a fortune and much of our savings had now been eaten up – I wasn't sure that we could afford for her to stay any longer, and yet what choice did we have? To pull her from the programme before she was ready would be to throw it all away. She would then have to live with the burden of failure.

I felt a deep resentment towards Emily – we had given her everything, every chance in life, and then more, and still it seemed it was not enough.

What did this say about the programme? Has it failed for Emily? Had all of this been in vain? If so, then where did we go from here? (Or rather, where did I go from here because that is how it usually works!) I seriously could not think of anything more we could do for this child.

### DAY EIGHTY-NINE 29<sup>th</sup> July: SOUTH GATE

*Today was a cool day. I got off separates which was the best thing that's happened!*

*We had Harry Potter read to us last night which was really awesome. I miss books but when I get my fires I will hopefully be able to call out a book!!*

*Today we climbed half of Indian. It was really hard work. The water tastes sooooo good!*

*Connor was a dick to Clare about the cancer story thing (Clare had pretended to her school and friends back home* that she had cancer and was going to die. Everyone believed her and accepted that as a reason for her not attending school. When her parents found out they went mad. Connor teased her about this all the time.) *I hope it has all been resolved. Clare will hopefully be graduating on Sunday, which would be awesome for her. She earned it fair and square.*

## COOMBE HILL

Facing the next day was really, really hard. I lay in bed for ages, unwilling to get up. All my good intentions of starting things anew went out of the window as I wallowed in self-pity.

The chap from around the corner, who Emily calls her boyfriend, called in with a letter for me to take to Utah. He's a good lad and wants to try to help her, but he is off to university soon and never saw them as being in a 'relationship' as Emily did. Nevertheless, he had written to her offering his support as a friend. I was in such a state it was embarrassing. I could hardly speak to him. Also, the phone was constantly ringing with friends wishing me well for the next day's trip and I was trying to tackle the miserable task of cancelling all our plans.

A dark mood descended like a cloud and I coped with the day by just switching off any emotion. Gradually I became numb to the whole thing. By the time of our conference call to Emily's therapist I had almost nothing to say.

We had a long conversation about why Emily had failed to graduate and it really seemed that she had deliberately sabotaged the opportunity by refusing to cooperate, refusing to get on with getting her coals (even though they had separated her from the rest of the group) and, in spite of having completed her assignment work, not handing it in. There was a lot of talk about the possibility that, subconsciously anyway, she did not want to leave the programme. She had come to feel safe and secure there and was perhaps frightened about the prospect of facing the real world again.

It was agreed that Jonathan and I should compose a letter to her, outlining all the consequences of her failing to graduate – all the heartache and pain we had been caused, the cancellation of flights and travel plans, the need for Tom to go away with friends, the huge cost implications, Jonathan's work commitments (meetings rearranged involving many others), cancellation of the trip to LA (a party for her) the difficulties of rearranging the trip for a later date, and so on. This letter would be given to her at the moment the others in her group left the camp to graduate.

### DAY NINETY: LOWER PINTOW

*Today was a cool day. We hiked seven miles from South*

Gate to Pintow. It was a fun day. We saw Melissa and Eleanor again. I hope they grad. They both deserve it. I'm going to miss them all so much when I go home. Even though I'll probably be seeing Chris (Virgin Wolf) in California.

Freaking Will and Clare are graduating tomorrow. I'm going to be really upset but they also do deserve it and I will be happy for them.

## DAY NINETY-ONE: LOWNE PINE

Today sucked balls big time. We got up and it rained so we put up a shelter for no reason because then we just packed up camp and started to hike. The hike was OK. It was easy.

Today was grad. Clare and Will have graduated. I got a letter from my parents (no comment). It really upset me a lot. Then Joe said that everything always revolved around me. He's such a freaking jerk. He just says sarcastic comments and is just really hurting me at the moment and pissing me off. I hate it. I hate everything.

Me, me, me, me, me,

It's all about me

I'm so frustrated and upset

Why can't anyone see?

## COOMBE HILL

Jonathan came down for the weekend and we tried to talk, but I was falling apart and just took to my bed – my sanctuary in distress. I wept and wept. I am so tired of crying all the time but I just could not seem to pull myself together. I could feel that I was in danger of spiralling down into the depths again. In spite of all the efforts I had made over the last three months I was suddenly aware that it was all very fragile. I had been trying hard to separate my needs from those of my family, rather than viewing myself as part of them all, and not allowing myself to lose control, but I was clearly still such a novice – one real test of my progress and I dissolved into a heap once more.

There was no way I could be on my own this week. Tom had to go ahead with his plans to go away so, although he was on summer holidays, I would not even have him to enjoy. In the end my father and Sue suggested that I just get in the car and go down to them. It was the best idea possible.

I spent a few days just walking in the Cotswolds. Come rain, shine and thunderstorms, Harry and I stomped up hills, through woodlands and along ridges with the most wonderful views out across Gloucestershire towards the Bristol Channel.

In the evenings I sat and talked with Dad and Sue and they helped me to regain my perspective on things. Sue spoiled me with lovely food and I gradually recovered my strength. By the time I got home I felt much more grounded and ready to face the next stage of the journey.

### DAY NINETY-TWO: LOWNE PINE

*Today sucked. I woke up really homesick. I just want to go home. We had a crap time here at RCA and I feel like I have earned the right to go home. I miss my mum sooooo much. I hate it. I wrote a letter back to my dad today. It sucked to have to write to him and say sorry about not graduating and what happened.*

*Somebody left out an onion and half a potato. They didn't fess up* (confess) *to it which really pissed me off. We saw Earth Warrior today. That was cool.*

### DAY NINETY-THREE: LOWNE PINE

*I can't get a coal anymore.*

There are no more journal entries. Emily says she ripped them up. She stayed one hundred days in the Redcliff Ascent Programme. A lot longer than most students, but not a record.

**Phase Seven Solo Reports:**

*I think I did OK in my life until I tried drinking and drugs for the first time. It has turned my life around. I used to be such a good little girl but I kept thinking to myself and talking to my friends about going out and getting drunk. That led to us all going out and getting drunk whenever we could and that was pretty much almost every night and whenever we got drunk we'd always go do something that would get us into trouble with the police.*

*If I died tomorrow people would probably write how much they loved me (like my parents) and how I'd tried really, really hard to get through this programme and become a better person for myself and others.*

*My mum would curse the drugs because if it wasn't for that I would not be here and wouldn't have died. My parents would say that I was a very kind and gentle little soul that always made them smile. She would always bring light to our eyes when she came home. Emily is a wonderful girl who had a lot going for her in life. She could have grown up to be a skier or an artist or a psychologist. She had so many talents and hobbies it was hard to keep up with them. But when the drinking started it all disappeared and I felt like my daughter was a different person. I just hope she made the changes she wanted to.*

*My friends would be upset, especially my two best friends, Olivia and Sammie. They were all so proud of me for coming to RCA and they are all waiting for me to go back and see them. Sammie and Olivia are awesome and I hope that if I do die someday they will always remember me.*

**Phase Seven Goals:**

1. *Finish this programme successfully – I'm concentrating thoroughly on all my phases and working really hard.*

2. *Go back to school – study over the rest of the summer ready for exams.*

3. *Climb Mount Everest – while travelling, save and raise money to go.*

4. *Travel the world.*

5. *Finish school well, get good grades so I can earn a gap year to travel in.*

6. *To become someone that can help teenagers with problems like I had.*

7. *Study hard and get a degree.*

8. *To be the world's best downhill racer (skiing) or slalom – keep training with the British Ski Association.*

9. *Teach kids how to race professionally – train and maybe teach at the ski club in Scotland for a season.*

10. *Give up drugs – don't let the temptations get to me.*

11. *Live a long, happy, successful life.*

12. *Do everything to the best of my ability. Work hard and enjoy myself. Stay healthy.*

**Phase Eight Reports:**

**Autobiography 8:**

Love is a nice feeling you get when you know that somebody really likes and cares a lot about you. Examples of love are such as the love between a mother and daughter, father and son, a married couple, a young couple. There is the love you have between you and your pets (like my dog and I). There are all different examples of love.

The examples I have thought about the most out here is the love and respect you give other individuals.

In the past I thought the whole world revolved around me. I had no respect for anyone. In order to love someone you have to respect them too. I guess I got the love part but not the respect bit. I love my parents – I always have. I just have not shown them love in a very good and affectionate way – I hurt them both so much.

All the things I did were for myself and only myself. I was

*soooooo selfish and had absolutely no respect for them. Of course I love them but I was just letting things get to me then I would take it out, especially on my mum.*

*My mum's the best person in the world and now I realise I was being totally out of order. When I get home I want to love them in all the possible ways I can. I love them so much.*

*Medicine Shield*

*I will always love you.*
*I will always love and treat people with kindness and respect.*
*I will go back to school and really concentrate on becoming an artist.*
*I'm going to succeed in life and fulfil my dreams.*
*I'm going to tackle all the obstacles that life throws at me.*
*I'm going to be strong and stand on my own two feet.*

*The medicine shield is a symbol of hope. A start of a new beginning to the rest of my life. It is preparing me and making me think about the changes I have made since I have been out here. It is also a reminder of how I am going to understand situations in life better and how I am going to deal with them.*

*It is a shield that represents the strength I feel I have now and it is there to protect me from all the temptations in life.*

# Chapter 22

## 5th August – COOMBE HILL

At our conference call this evening we heard that, having crashed and burned, Emily had finally decided to pull everything together. She would definitely be graduating on 16th August. The timing had become critical as we had agreed that she needed to have some time at home before going off to St. Mary's School, Shaftesbury, Dorset, in September. (This was the boarding school, which I had wanted Emily to go to some eighteen months before. We had kept in touch and they were prepared to give her a trial term.)

I didn't dare to get excited, or even look ahead much more than a day at a time. Jonathan remade all the travel plans and I just focussed on staying calm and not thinking much. I busied myself with all sorts of things around the house like carpet cleaning, tasks I would not normally get around to doing. I didn't feel like seeing anyone. Everyone thought I was in the States anyway. I wasn't depressed; I was simply holding on to myself and getting through the days until we could get on a plane.

## 12th August – COOMBE HILL

Perry came to collect Harry and I drove down to Wiltshire to meet with Jonathan's parents who were going to look after Tom while we were in the States. Poor Tom. I couldn't help but feel he had become a parcel – passed around from place to place. Still, he is fond of his grandparents and I was certain that they would have a nice time together.

I had not seen Betty and John since Jonathan and I split up, and the meeting was awkward. These people have been so wonderful to me over the years but Jonathan has always shielded them from the harsher realities in our family so they never had a very coherent picture of what was going on. It was therefore difficult for them to understand what was happening now. I have always felt that it was deceitful of Jonathan to manage them in this way – even though he claims that it is to protect them. They are effectively kept out of the loop, which has meant that, as time has gone on, there is more and more that they don't know. This has meant that our relationship has become false. Although I love them and want to sit down and tell them everything I don't have the right to do so. I couldn't wait to get away.

Driving back home I reflected on how they must be feeling. Jonathan's wife had 'lost it' and couldn't deal with their lovely children. And now she had chucked him out of their home. I don't really think they would view me so harshly but I knew their views on marriage well enough to realise that they would find it hard to accept what I had done, and the possible impact it would have on the children. I contemplated writing to them, and composed a letter in my head while I was driving, but I never wrote it. I couldn't find the right words.

## 13<sup>th</sup> August – LONDON TO PHOENIX, ARIZONA

Friday, 13<sup>th</sup>!! Jonathan had come down from Manchester last night and was busy packing. Then we took a taxi to the airport and boarded the flight to Phoenix, Arizona, the first leg of our journey.

Jonathan had been very loving during the weekend before I went to my dad's, when I had been in pieces, and I was able to feel much more comfortable with him than I had expected. While walking in the Cotswolds I became aware that I was not as angry with him as I had been. I even fantasised that there might be a chance of reconciliation. But there was so much going on in my head at the time that I knew I was not thinking very straight, so I tucked the thought away. Above all else I knew I needed space and time on my own to work things through. I was too fragile to be making any major decisions.

We talked a lot on the plane and I began to realise, for the first time in months, that I could relax with Jonathan. However, I still felt very guarded and strangely insecure. I had to watch any signals that I might be giving him as I didn't think it would be reasonable to allow him any false hope at this stage. Everything was still raw, and I was too uncertain. The only thing I was really sure of was that if I gave in, and we got back together, things couldn't just go back to how they were before. I wouldn't be able to take it. It would break me.

But I also desperately wanted to love and be loved. I felt that I had tried to give everything to our relationship – to be the perfect wife and mother – and look what had happened! I knew that Jonathan loves me, but our love for each other had become so destructive, a vortex of chaos from which I longed to escape. Yet it was very hard to let go of twenty years of trying to build a marriage.

We landed in Phoenix, picked up a hire car and headed north to Sedona. I love this part of America and had many happy memories of the last time we had been there. One summer while we were living in Washington we took a wonderful trip starting in Santa Fe and going up to Taos, Durango, Monument Valley, Bryce Canyon, and the Grand Canyon. It was a spectacular trip through some of the most amazing scenery – red rocks, desert plains, huge skies and dramatic weather. We ended the trip at a resort in Sedona called 'Enchantment' (a tacky name, but actually quite apt) and I fell in love with it all. Now, eight years on, we were heading back to Enchantment to recharge our batteries and to prepare for the trip to Utah.

The resort had expanded over the years but was every bit as wonderful as we had remembered. Little red adobe-style apartments huddled in a narrow canyon between the most awe-inspiring red mountains, which glow in the sunset like burning embers. There is a powerful sense of electricity in the air which is so vibrant you can almost touch it. Lightning flashes across the landscape, giving the place a huge sense of drama, and having a curious energising effect on even the most beaten of spirits.

Sedona is a really special place for me, and if ever there had been a perfect time to be there, this was it.

## 15th August – SEDONA TO UTAH

The next leg of our trip was a five-hour drive north to St George, Utah.

Leaving the red rock mountains behind us we headed up through Oak Creek Canyon, following a precipitous route steeply upwards through heavy forests, dark and cool, until we reached Flagstaff. From there the landscape changed dramatically as we cut up through the Painted Desert, with the Navaho Indian Reservation on our right and the Grand Canyon National Park to the left. The Reservation is a rocky, barren wilderness dotted with hamlets of shacks and abandoned cars. A desolate landscape, given to the Navaho nation by the United States Government, in exchange for their free run of the plains and deserts.

As our eyes became accustomed to the landscape we began to appreciate the beauty of these wasted lands, and I soon lost myself in daydreams of the Native American Indians and their culture, which formed such an integral part of the programme at Redcliff Ascent. I envied Emily's immersion in all the richness and purity of the Indian traditions, their lives governed by nature and natural laws.

As we left the desert plains and climbed into the mountains through the Kaibab National Forest the views became breathtakingly vast. There is just nothing here. No towns or villages, just acres of nothingness, and the Hurricane Cliffs rising out of the plain in front of us. Once we climbed into these majestic mountains we were surprised to find that we were as high as 8,000 metres above sea-level. The air was thin and clear and, apart from the odd Harley Davidson, we were almost the only ones on the road. The sheer space and scale of it all was quite overwhelmingly beautiful.

Finally, in time for supper, we reached St George. Mormon country. Having seen very little civilisation for hours, we were amazed to find a large town, and a clearly flourishing civilisation, in what appeared to be the middle of nowhere. Huge housing projects were being developed in every direction. Advertising billboards boasted loudly of golf resorts, sailing centres, new hotels and many other messages of fast-increasing prosperity.

Too tired to explore, and with such a huge day ahead of us, we had a good meal, retreated into our rather sanitised hotel and tried to get some sleep.

## 16th August – ST GEORGE, UTAH

We made an early start, as we had to be at the Redcliff Ascent offices by 9.00 am for our parenting conference. I was so nervous and full of expectation that I could hardly take in the trip to Enterprise, and have very little memory of the one-and-a-half hour drive except that, once we reached the St George city limits, we were back into the empty landscapes of yesterday.

At about nine o'clock we came to the crossroads at Enterprise, to discover that that was pretty much all there was! Enterprise is made up of the Redcliff Ascent Headquarters (two large airport-style hangars), a petrol station, a clutch of small homes and Marve's Burger Bar.

We met up with the parents of other students graduating that day. This was difficult, as the last thing I felt like doing was being sociable. It became apparent that all eight sets of parents had come from far and wide, both geographically and socially, and I began to get drawn into their stories. Mostly, they were Americans; from Virginia, Texas, Seattle, California, Connecticut and New Mexico. Then there was a couple from Germany, and the two of us from England. We were about as different as a group of people can be, except that we all had children in the programme, and we had all scraped together enough money to give our troubled kids a chance to straighten out their lives.

Doc Dan, Daniel Sanderson, clinical psychologist and leader of the programme, took us through five hours of intense lectures and seminars which left our minds reeling. It also brought us together as a group, as we shared our experiences, and our knowledge of what had brought us and our children to the point where there was nothing left to do for them but this.

Although each situation and each child is unique, what struck me was the similarity of our journeys. Interestingly, six out of the eight who were about to graduate had had a diagnosis of ADHD (Attention Deficit Hyperactive Disorder) or ADD (Attention Deficit Disorder). At some point, usually about the age of 7, our children had become discernibly different to other children and, commonly, dropped out of school as a result, leading to diagnosis. At the onset of puberty, the solutions we had previously sought came unstuck and our children gradually came off the rails, vulnerable to substance abuse, violence or danger. Emily, at 14 when she arrived at the programme, now only just 15, was one of the youngest, but the patterns towards crisis were remarkably similar.

Every single family had spent years battling for medical and psychiatric support, while trying to keep the kids in school and lead as normal a life as possible (often for the sake of other siblings). We had all combed books and the Internet, desperate for solutions, so we were all very knowledgeable. Yet each one of us, in particular the mothers, had reached the depths of hopelessness, despair and breakdown (either personal or family breakdown, often both).

It goes without saying that we were all willing to do absolutely anything that would help our kids and our families. I have never been in such an intensely focussed group.

Doc Dan brought together all the threads of our experiences into a model of development, which could be applied to each child.

I wish I could remember the exact words of Dan's teachings, but I don't think I can give an accurate or substantial enough report to do him justice. Suffice to say that the critical elements revolve around the child's natural development from an egocentric infant, who sees himself as the centre of his universe, and his struggle for power and influence throughout childhood and the teenage years, which eventually, in adulthood, should lead to the development of life skills such as individuation, self responsibility and ultimately control over his own life.

For whatever reason (ADHD, life trauma, abuse) our children have taken a 'Developmental Holiday' (missing out on crucial stages in normal development) and, although maturing in other ways, remain stuck at the egocentric stage of development, continuing to see themselves as the centre of the universe. Unable to earn the right to their parents' trust, and thus gain influence within the family in a normal way, they learn to 'steal' that influence in whatever way they can.

Because we love them and want them to feel worthy, we, the parents, find ourselves drawn into coping strategies, which look like love and caring but are, in fact, enabling our children to perpetuate their egocentric behaviour. (This all related back to the learning I did in England about co-dependency.)

I can feel some of the elements of this thinking in my own situation. When I realised that Emily could not cope socially, my mother 'lioness' instinct – to protect her from hurt –meant that she never learned to fight her own corner. Once she was diagnosed as ADHD I learned that there were things she could not do naturally, like control herself, and so I began a pattern of parenting which compensated for her lack of control. I defended her from the other mothers at school; I fought for special attention for her from teachers, and so on. Thus, where was her motivation to take responsibility for her own actions? 'Mummy will always love me, she will always rescue me and make things OK.'

As she grew, Emily remained egocentric, but also learned to wield power in the family because she needed 'more' support than other kids. Consequently she became omnipotent. Instead of developing a personal 'mission statement' for her life, something to motivate her and drive her decisions, Emily just remained in the moment. No goal, no commitment, no motivation and thus no self-development. The worse she behaved, the more she expected me to compensate. The result was that she never really developed a proper sense of self and so, when others around her (peers, teachers, parents) objected to her totally unreasonable life strategy, she just pitched headlong into a vortex of self-destruction and expected someone else (her mother usually) to pick up the pieces.

As the negative life experiences pile up the child locks them away and focuses only on the public persona which he or she has built up to hide the vulnerable 'little child' inside. But the experiences that have been locked away continue to have an influence, generating fear or sadness within. We, as parents, are not allowed access to the fear or sadness. Instead we see anger (or 'I'm fine'). I can see now that Emily was probably using anger to hide her emotions, but she was making her anger my problem, and expecting me to repair it. Thus she felt I was failing her when I was not dealing with it either.

Emily's omnipotent position within the family has rocked its very foundations. Her strength of personality and constant need for attention saps everyone's energy.

Eventually we all stumbled out into the heat of the day, dazed by hours of intense concentration and revelation. We then had to collect our equipment for a night camping out in the desert, and load our stuff onto the Redcliff bus for the journey out to Base Camp. The bus, a characterful heap of junk, which threatened not to start, was soon on its way, radio blaring; as if we were a bunch of holidaymakers off for the day.

But we were not on holiday, we were a group of parents who had not seen our children for a long time (Emily's 100 days was the longest) and who were not sure what they would find when they were reunited. Although we were all tense with excitement, the events of the morning had made us strangely intimate as a group, and the atmosphere was curiously festive.

# Chapter 23

★ ✪ ★

We waved goodbye to civilisation and bumped along a deeply rutted road, across a railway line and on through a maze of dirt roads into the wilderness. The landscape was amazing. Huge sky, sagebrush and juniper trees, rocks and boulders, (hence the state of the bus, I suspect), and distant blue-grey mountains. In all this harshness our daughter had been living – hiking in the mountains and across the plains, sleeping rough and eating from a campfire pot. For 100 days! What an incredible experience.

If we thought Enterprise was in the middle of nowhere, the base camp was an hour and a half further on into nowhere. It consisted of a thatched communal open-sided hut, a plank and rope bridge across a small ravine, a stone circle and amphitheatre and (oh joy!) what looked like latrines. This was it. This is where the groups met for communal events like 'shindig 'and this is where we would be spending the next 24 hours!

Fire Drum (our driver and now our host and master of ceremonies) parked the bus and we all clambered out into the dusty heat. Across the clearing a pathway, marked with stones, snaked up and around the hill and we assembled at the bottom of the path full of expectation. Having watched some of the Brat Camp series on television, I had a reasonable idea of what to expect. The students were sitting in a 'kiva' (a Native Indian contemplation pit) at the top of the hill and would be called out in turn to run the half mile down the path and into the arms of their parents.

Fire Drum radioed up to the 'kiva' and then we heard a shout that they were ready. We all shouted back and then, emotions running high, there was silence as we waited.

First down on the run-in was Emily. Everyone clapped and cheered as she ran into our arms. The three of us hugged until we thought we would break. This child of ours, dirty and bedraggled, tear-stained and looking like an Indian squaw with her beads and dungarees, was safe and sound. I was so happy I thought I would burst.

Before long, the next one came down to applause and shouting, and another, then another until each family had been reunited with their child. Tears flowed freely and there was much laughter and hugging all round. Everyone was euphoric. It was such a tender moment that it is hard to describe it even now without fresh tears.

Gradually the families split away and went off individually with their children. Emily was so overexcited that we rushed about aimlessly before agreeing to go for a walk. She insisted that we take turns to carry her pack so we could appreciate what she had

had to carry. We then went off to explore what had become her world.

Emily took us up to the 'kiva' to show us where she had waited for the run-in. I hardly made it up the hill with her pack, it was so heavy, and that was without food and water supplies. She looked across the landscape and pointed out all the mountains she had referred to in her letters. She seemed so happy and 'at home' here, confident and eager to make sure we saw as much as possible. Her news bubbled up out of her like a brook and it was hard to keep up as she jumped from one thing to another. Last night she had spent on solo and had hiked to Outpost that afternoon, arriving just a short while before we did. They had listened out for the bus and saw our dust in the distance as they climbed down into the 'kiva' to wait for us. She was magical to be with – I couldn't hear enough about her adventures out here, even if I was a little surprised by the American accent she had acquired. (Strange to me because when she was little she had an East Coast accent and this was much more drawn-out and south-western.)

When we rejoined the others, Fire Drum organised a few games, which were great fun. We chased each other around, shrieking and laughing, just out of sheer joy at being together and sharing a very special moment in our lives.

Then, each family had to make a bow-drill fire for a communal fire to cook our supper on. While Jonathan struggled with the palm stone, bow and fireboard, Emily and I went to find tree bark to make into nests for the coals. One by one the lighted coals were added to make a communal fire and supper got under way.

As a huge pot of pasta stew cooked its way to edibility each family organised their stuff into a camp for the night. We sloped off to get the best of the sunset – streaks of pink and orange against a vast sky contained by the dark purple of mountain peaks. It was truly beautiful; truly, as they say in the States, awesome!

After the pasta stew, followed by peach cobbler, both of which were delicious and most welcome, we arranged ourselves around the fire, and Fire Drum took charge of the proceedings.

Fire Drum began with a very special story. I can't remember the name of the tribe of Indians, but the story went something like this:

Their chief died and his son, who was due to succeed him, was still only quite young. Some of the tribe wanted to stick with their tradition of the son succeeding the father, but others were scornful that the boy was not wise or strong enough to be their leader.

Tradition had it that the aspiring chief must run naked through the ceremoniously assembled tribe, so they might know him, and down to the river where he must dive in and prove he had touched the river bed by bringing up a stone from the bottom.

The young brave was determined. Since it was winter the river was frozen over and a hole had to be cut in the ice. He ran naked through the tribe, dived through the hole and fought to get to the riverbed. But he ran out of breath and was forced to surface without the required trophy. He had failed. Some of the tribe were disappointed, as they had wanted him to succeed, others felt proved right – he was inadequate to be their chief.

The next day the brave tried again. As he ran through the tribe he noticed there were far fewer witnesses than yesterday, as many felt certain he would not succeed. He dived through the hole in the ice and tried with all his might to get to the bottom for his trophy but, once again, was forced to the surface empty handed.

On the third day the brave tried again. This time, the entire tribe turned out to watch, curious now about a brave who would be so persistent. As before, the brave ran naked through the gathering and down to the river. He dived through the hole and fought with all his strength and might to get down to the riverbed. He returned to the edge of the ice hole with a handful of silt and a precious stone. Triumphant, he walked back to his tipi with the tribe celebrating him and his victory.

This brave became chief of the tribe and was forever remembered as a wise and strong leader. Tales of his courage became legendary.

The rest of the evening was spent exchanging stories of a different kind. Each person had to tell of their best and worst days during the programme so, in this way, the students and parents each learned of the others' joys and sorrows. Some stories were funny and some desolate; but we all shared in each other's journeys.

Eventually each family settled down for the night under a sky filled with stars as big as dinner plates and we fell asleep with Emily hugged in tight in her 'wiggi' between us.

## 17th August – 'REDCLIFF ASCENT', UTAH

I awoke, stiff and cold but very, very happy. I had missed the dawn but the sky was still streaked with pink and clear. I lay there going over the events of the day before. Everything was so surreal. The rest of the world seemed far, far away and it was as if this morning was all there was, nothing else mattered. Fire Drum was playing a pipe and the music was soothing and melodic. Emily stirred beside me and I turned to hug her.

Emily and the other graduates were in charge of cooking

breakfast so Jonathan and I went for a walk. I had nothing to say. I just wanted to 'be' in this moment'. It was so beautiful here and I could have been persuaded to stay forever.

As we walked back to the camp we could see there was going to be a ceremony of some kind. My heart quickened as Emily had written that the biggest honour for a student was to be 'named'.

Sure enough, Emily and two others were called and the ceremony began. Fire Drum, Crystal Moon and another staff member, whose name I can't now recall, spoke of the achievements and personal qualities of each in turn, burned sage brush around their body and invited each to step out of their old bodies and into their new spiritual bodies. Each was christened with a Native Indian name, which described their new spirit. It was all so moving I could hardly breathe. Emily became 'Laughing Star'.

'Laughing Star' and the others then proceeded to serve a celebration breakfast of sausages and pancakes with syrup. We ate until we were fit to burst.

Once breakfast was cleared away and we had all helped to pack up the camp, each student's therapist arrived to have a final session with them and their parents. Doc Chris, however, did not appear, and we had to radio the offices to see where she was. Unfortunately she had had a personal crisis and would not be able to see us. Instead, Doc Dan, who had also done some work with Emily, came out to talk to us.

This was an important session as it is vital for the student to agree a way forward with the parents. Both student and parents need to 'buy in' to the changes that must be made at home in order for the student to continue the work they have done at Redcliff. It would be too easy to argue about who said what, or who did what – the therapist's job is to mediate in drawing up a plan or agreement which needs to be signed by all parties.

Doc Dan took us through the psychological assessment he had made of Emily and it became clear that there were quite a few areas which still needed to be addressed. She had made good progress at Redcliff and had been provided with a tool kit of skills to use to change her life. However, the issue of her omnipotence needed to be resolved before she could move forward developmentally. We had to agree to be careful (me in particular) that the commitment we make to change is equal on all sides. It had been too easy for me to give total commitment, and for Emily to give none. If this continued, we would simply go back to the situation where my excess commitment begins to compensate for her lack and we start the downward spiral of my taking responsibility for her actions, leaving her free to do as she pleases.

None of us expected the solution to be a piece of cake but after the lectures yesterday I realised that, without Jonathan's physical presence at home, it would be largely up to me to deal with this. 'Tough Love' does not end when the programme ends. I hoped I had the strength and the courage to carry it through the next phase.

Until this point I think I had regarded Emily's graduation as the end of 'the long dark days' and I had hoped for new beginnings. Jonathan and I have often argued about the principle of 'wiping the slate clean'. He had always insisted that it is important to be able to do this – to begin with a clean slate and move forward. I had always maintained that you couldn't negate the past. All that you do, you take forward in your life – good and bad. Fresh starts can be made, but they can only be made once you have recognised and dealt with the past, it is the process of dealing with it that allows you to move forward.

In this instance it seemed that I was right. We were not looking at new beginnings because Emily, Jonathan and I had not dealt fully with what brought us here. Yes, we had now all done a lot of recognising what each of us did to contribute to the chaos, but we had not necessarily dealt with it. We were looking at a continuation of the process started here at Redcliff for Emily. We had not reached the end of the journey, but had just got to a major milestone, pausing to get our breath back before moving on.

I found this very daunting.

The Redcliff programme could not 'fix' Emily. What it had done, though, was to interrupt the negative, downward spiral that had driven her into a mission of self-destruction. It had taught her that life has boundaries, and that there are consequences to not keeping within those boundaries. It had provided her with important survival skills, which have given her courage and belief in herself, and her ability to take control of her life, yet to take responsibility for her actions. It had also restored her self-respect and taught her to respect others. In a way it had allowed her to rediscover the essence of herself which had always been there and which had sustained our love for her, no matter how bad things got, no matter what she did. The programme had given her these things which we, her parents, had failed to give her, no matter how hard we tried.

What we now saw in Emily was a happy and confident child, in charge of herself. Someone we could hug and who wanted to be hugged.

After our session with Doc Dan (a truly special person) we took ourselves off up the hill to continue talking. We climbed down into the 'kiva' contemplation pit and sat on the 'altar' while Emily taught us all about life in the wilderness: mountains climbed, people in her group, staff she loved and those she hated, mustangs running through the camp, jack-rabbits, snakes, and medicinal cures for sore feet and bruises. It was wonderful to have her introduce us to a world that was hers, and not ours. She had been through things that we never had and probably never would. So often, parents are more knowledgeable than the child, but out here, Emily was the expert.

When we got back to the camp the other families were playing games and, as we stood watching, we heard the bus in the distance. Our time here was coming to an end. We took a walk across the rope and plank bridge, up a dry ravine and back around the camp. I began to wonder how Emily would be feeling about leaving this place and hoped it would not be too hard for her. There was something special here which made you feel serene and anchored to the earth, as if in some way you were contained and safe. Going back to the hustle and bustle of urban life might be quite frightening for her.

We loaded up the bus and soon set off back down the dirt roads towards civilisation. Emily pointed out lots of things en route that stirred memories for her of different hikes and deathmarches: 'this is where I fell down and refused to go on.' 'That's where the water hole is.' and so on. We drank it all in and saved it for the future.

The radio was on and the atmosphere in the bus was celebratory. Suddenly I picked up a familiar song – James Brown's 'I feel good, I got you'. I asked Fire Drum to turn up the volume and soon the whole bus was shouting out the lyrics. It's a great song; it spans the generations and captured the moment perfectly.

# Chapter 24

Back at the Redcliff offices in Enterprise there was a whole round of things to be done. We unloaded the bus and returned our bedrolls, the kids went off for showers and a medical and we parents went through all the paperwork and signed our kids out. Emily appeared fresh from a shower and in her own clothes – lovely as ever. But it was going to take more than one shower to wash away the dust of the desert!

Far from being desperate to leave, all the kids spun out their good byes to the staff. This great team of people had obviously built strong, and often intimate, relationships with their charges. Lots of promises were made to return.

Eventually we all agreed to go down the road to Marve's for a farewell burger which, we were told, is a tradition for graduation day. Only one family was unable to come as they had a flight to catch. One of the noticeable things about the kids was their obsession with food – and many were desperate for a junk food fix. This tiny burger bar probably did a month's business in the two hours we were there, as the kids indulged themselves in foods they had been denied during their time in the wilderness. We have some great photos of the stacks of fries, burgers (they did a special Redcliff Burger which was gigantic), shakes, cokes and so on.

Finally, though, it was definitely time to go. Addresses and e-mails were exchanged on napkins and the hugging looked like it would last forever. Then we pulled away from the parking lot, and began the next phase of our journey.

We took a different route back to Sedona so that we could drive through the Zion National Park, which is stunningly beautiful, then on to Page and Lake Powell before heading south. Initially each of us was lost in our own thoughts, taking in the scenery and probably re-running the events of the last two days. Then Emily decided that she needed some music but, try as I might, I could find nothing she wanted to hear on the radio. This triggered a fierce outburst from her – our first real threat to the 'new beginning'. She had already begun to show signs of trying to push Jonathan around and now she challenged him directly. His response was measured, not angry as it might have been in the past, but nevertheless, it broke the dam wall and the tears began. Emily cried and cried and cried. She got so hysterical that we had to pull off the road. I felt instinctively that she just needed to let all the tension go and so we stood in the afternoon sun and left her alone. Eventually she calmed down and I suggested that she try to sleep for a bit.

We continued our journey through Marble Canyon, with the Echo

Cliffs on our left and the sun setting in front of us. At some points the cliffs come so close and are so high that you feel there is no exit to the canyon and that you will drive straight into the cliffs. Then suddenly, at the last moment, the sunset broke through the narrow gap and we were back into the plains. It was a spectacular feeling. As we drove on towards a sky on fire with the sunset, Emily started to read us letters she had received at Redcliff, her autobiography, and parts of her journals. It was an unforgettable journey.

By the time we reached Oak Creek Canyon it was dark, and when we got to Sedona the fire red of the mountains was fading into blackness. Emily recognised Enchantment from eight years ago (when she was only 7 years old), and was delighted to be there. The storms of earlier had passed and she was calm, but totally exhausted. She collapsed into bed – her first real bed in 101 days. She seemed determined to sleep with us but we finally managed to persuade her that she would enjoy her own bed more. We tucked her in and she eventually fell asleep

## 18th August – 'ENCHANTMENT', SEDONA

We all slept late. The last few days had been so huge. The intensity and emotional turmoil of our Redcliff experience, the sheer vividness of it all, not to mention the miles travelled and the landscapes crossed. I felt like a wrung-out dishcloth.

Eventually Jonathan got up and went off to the gym, while I sat out on the balcony in the hot sun and contemplated the magical red mountains, which dominated my view. Once again I felt the energy of this very special place and hoped that it would have the same effect on Emily and give her the strength to face the outside world again.

When Emily woke up she was a bit freaked out, not in a hyperactive way, but everything seemed to be too stimulating for her. She turned on the television but it made her very agitated to watch it. She said she felt that everything on the screen was jumping at her –making her feel bombarded by images. I suggested that she should take things very slowly and not expect to be able to leap back into life as it was before. She was clearly not ready to face the outside world and we were just going to have to let her take her time.

Emily spent an age in the shower and then she and I struggled to get her hair tidied up. It was so matted and coarse, it felt like dreadlocks! But, with the wonders of hair conditioner, and a great deal of patience with a comb, we managed to untangle it. It had been streaked by the sun in a way that she would once have begged me to pay for in a hair salon! She looked wonderful.

Food was never far from her mind during these days, yet she was unwilling to face the restaurant. We decided to go into Sedona and shop at Safeways instead. We had a kitchen and a barbecue so we could just stay in our little adobe house until she felt ready to see other people.

Emily had so much fun in Safeways, rushing up and down the aisles to find her favourite foods. It was funny to see her choosing all the things that had been great treats or rewards at Redcliff – peanut butter, Monterey Jack cheese, pasta packets; but she drew the line at trail mix and oats! As we reached the checkout we became aware that it was raining – not simply raining, but pouring down. Jonathan went to get the car, as already the car park was flooding. We were all in a rather silly mood and Emily and I were dancing around in the ridiculously wide entrance to the store amazed at the sheets of water, thunder and lightening. Jonathan decided the only possible way to get us safely into the car without being electrocuted by the storm was to back the car right into the entrance to the store. Other shoppers could not believe what he was doing, but we didn't care, and we left Safeways in fits of laughter at the ridiculous situation.

The drive back to Enchantment was quite a thrill. Hailstones the size of small rocks were hurtling down onto the car roof, making so much noise that we had to shout at each other. The road ahead had become a river. We could not even see the red rocks above us as the hail was so intense, and pretty soon it looked as if the ground was covered in snow. The whole scene was surreal, even a bit frightening – if we couldn't get back to Enchantment we would be stuck in the canyon until the flooding subsided. However, we made it back to our adobe house, got soaked to the skin ferrying in the groceries, pulled up the drawbridge and snuggled down inside to watch the storm.

The weather raged for most of the day and it was so dark that it was hard to notice when evening came. We spent the rest of the day eating and dozing and generally indulging ourselves. I think we turned in early, although I can't quite remember.

## 19<sup>th</sup> August – ENCHANTMENT

We awoke to a hot and glorious day and I went for a walk to inspect the damage caused by the storm. Bits of tree and bush lay everywhere, red rock and silt were washed up all over the previously well-manicured grounds of the resort. Apparently the road through the canyon had been washed away – we were lucky we came back when we did. The red rocks gleamed with wet and the ground was steaming as the hot desert sun tried to dry everything out.

Emily still did not want to leave our little house and that was fine. We had planned to stay here for another three days and I was content just to be with her, and get used to having her with us. I swam, Jonathan took off to the gym and she just hung about getting used to the TV and resting. We talked a fair bit – more than we had done for a lot of months before Redcliff. I felt we had got her back after more than two years of complete chaos. It was a great feeling.

By extraordinary coincidence our friends, Debra, Tony and their two boys, old friends from England, had arrived at Enchantment the night before. They knew we were not being sociable but we agreed to meet for a drink at the bar in the evening.

It was lovely to see them – a blast from home in the midst of our pilgrimage to collect Emily. Surprisingly, Emily chose to join us, and they were delighted to see her. She only stayed for about 15 minutes, but it was a big step for her to get out of the room and face people. She was very charming. Even though we didn't stay long it was great to share a bottle of wine and feel relatively normal for a while. It was the first time Jonathan and I had seen anyone we knew together and, even though it was all a bit strange and stilted, they were lovely, and very understanding.

We went back and barbecued supper, then just sat around on the deck talking and looking at the red rocks until tiredness overtook us. Emily was again unwilling to sleep on her own but, with doors propped open and a light on, she eventually settled down.

## 20th August – ENCHANTMENT

Today was a rollercoaster. Emily was feeling a bit more herself and was beginning to test out the boundaries once more. It was like being back on eggshells again, not knowing how to react to her volatile mood swings. One minute she was happy and huggy; the next, antagonistic and challenging. She seemed to want to bury herself in the pop video channel on TV and just eat. She was severely testing Jonathan's mood and demanding constant attention. Jonathan and I agreed that we needed to start showing her that we were not going to allow this kind of behaviour to take a hold as it had done before, so we began to rein her in gently, making it clear that we were not going to accept this sort of treatment from her. We had to explain that her behaviour, not her, but her behaviour, had been sapping this family of all our generosity and all our energy, and that was no longer acceptable.

Our discussion with her seemed to open up all the old wounds and she totally lost it. She ranted and raved at us about everything she could think of. When we tried to bring her back to ground by reflecting on our discussions at Redcliff it seemed to be like a red rag to a bull. She started to deny lots of things that had been part of her therapy programme (as I had feared she would do because we had not had proper closure with her therapist) and she railed against the world, and us. Jonathan and I both kept calm throughout – as we had tried to do so often in the past, but had frequently failed. Inside, of course, our hearts were churning once more.

It was so distressing to see her like this again after all we had been through. It was so hard to consider the possibility that Redcliff had not been the success we had hoped it would be. Once again it felt as if we simply could not manage her, let alone reason with her. Not for the first time we were struggling with the thought that she might be mentally unstable. We just did not know what to do.

It was a miserable, miserable day.

## 21st August – ENCHANTMENT

Today was a little better, but not much. Yesterday was hard to recover from and I felt very desolate. Jonathan coped by believing that it was just a minor setback, but I had a sinking feeling that it was not going to turn out well.

Emily announced that we had to accept her for who she is and stop trying to force her to be someone else. This might sound reasonable, but we knew from experience that who she was, lacking any consideration of anyone else, was not an acceptable way to be. She could not lead her life expecting the world to compromise to her needs. We had never pushed her to do things just because we wanted her to be one thing or another, we were just trying to set some boundaries that would help her to find her way in life without too much pain. All we wanted was for her to be happy and able to take care of her own life. But we just didn't seem able to convince her of this.

This was to be our last day at Enchantment. Jonathan was going back to England tomorrow and the plan was for Emily and me to drive back to Los Angeles. I began to be concerned about the trip – a ten-hour drive across the desert via Palm Springs. I had hoped it would provide some space for us to talk, just be together and have some fun, but now it looked like it could be a nightmare. I clung to the hope that, once it was just the two of us, things might be easier, but I was now dreading the trip I had so looked forward to.

# Chapter 25

★ ✭ ★

## 22nd August – ON THE ROAD, SEDONA TO LOS ANGELES

We had to leave the resort early in order to get the best of the day on the road. Emily was rather sullen and our good byes to Jonathan were tense.

We took the road south to Phoenix and Emily found a hip-hop radio station, which blasted out for most of the way. At Phoenix we turned right onto Route 10 and headed west.

Tom and I had watched a movie together recently about 'road-racing' which he loved. It was filmed along Route 10, so much of the scenery was already familiar to me from the film. I thought of him now and hoped he was OK. He and Emily had spoken by phone last night and she had upset him. He, of course, was hoping for a 'repaired sister' and was very alarmed that she seemed no different, and had even been hurtful to him. She hadn't meant to, she had simply been thoughtless and told him he sounded like a girl. This was not tactful, especially as he had been hoping his voice would break any time now, and was beginning to think of himself as a teenager.

Jonathan was going back to spend some time with him at home, so I hoped that he would prepare Tom for Emily's return. The poor guy had had a tough year with all this, and was now enduring a summer holiday going from pillar to post, not having much time with either of his parents. He had never been one to complain, but I realised he had had a raw deal for too long now.

The road was wide and open, but soon after leaving Phoenix the traffic thinned out until we were almost on our own. The heat was intense, in spite of our air-conditioned car, and we slowly ate up the miles across the boring, dusty terrain. I made sure I stopped every two hours to have a break. I knew that driving for 10 hours would be physically demanding, but I was in the right mood to push myself. I had considered that I might stop for the night in Palm Springs if I got too tired, but I had to make it at least that far because there was nowhere of any size between there and Phoenix anyway.

Emily was lost to the radio and was very bad company. My dreams of an adventure together were completely shattered. I felt like a taxi driver, but I refused to let it get to me. Luckily, I found it quite easy to disappear into my own thoughts.

There isn't much between Phoenix and the Colorado River, which separates Arizona from California, and there is even less from there until you reach Indio. After that the casinos begin to rise up out of the desert and the mountain ranges come in a little closer – these are the Orocopia Mountains, or they could have been the

Little San Bernadino Mountains. I didn't care. The road was endless. By now I seriously hated hip-hop and had insisted on a bit of Joe Cocker and Lenny Kravitz for the sake of my sanity!

My thoughts drifted back over the last few months. There was no doubt I had come a long way from the gibbering wreck I had been in April of this year. I was more grounded. I had learned to enjoy being with myself and felt much stronger and happier than I had been for years. The steady drip, drip of dealing with Emily from day to day had worn me away, even before she went off the rails. It was no wonder that I had not been able to cope when things finally fell apart. I had stopped beating myself up for the terrible situation we were in and, once she was in Utah, I was able to start separating myself from her. I was determined not to go backwards. I desperately wanted now to be my own person. I felt I had spent too long trying to be everyone else's person and the results had been disastrous, not just for me, but for Emily and for Jonathan.

The last few days with Jonathan had seemed to throw me backwards. I felt uncomfortable with him – there remained so much that had been unresolved between us – and yet there were also moments when I was reminded of how we used to be, how we could have been still. In his own way he was trying really hard to make things better between us and I respected that. I also recognised that this last year had been impossible for him to deal with as well. We had both coped badly, and had ended up taking it out on each other. Was it reasonable to let our marriage dissolve because of this? Should we give each other another chance?

I was certain of one thing, we must not blame Emily for the breakdown of our marriage. This would be an easy option to choose, given what she has put us through, but it would be wrong. As adults we should have been able to manage our relationship, and ourselves, better than we had done. I looked at the girl sitting beside me in the car. My daughter. She was still very uncommunicative, but not hostile. She just didn't seem to feel the need to engage with me. Emily had certainly been the catalyst in the break-up of our relationship, but she couldn't be expected to carry the burden of having been the cause.

I realised now that I had switched off to Jonathan. With everything that had happened I had not been able to deal with the problems between us and therefore had blanked them out. Unable to cope with the enormity of everything at once I had withdrawn from our relationship. The more difficult he became, the more I was able to justify to myself that my reaction was reasonable. In the end the love just stopped.

But did love stop, or was it just on hold until I could find space to sort it all out? Could I fall in love with him again? I didn't know, but maybe it was possible and had to be worth a try. I needed space to work this out, and be certain that if we were to try to repair our relationship, and our marriage, that I could do it with full commitment.

My difficulty was that I felt under constant pressure to make a decision. From his point of view, he had been giving me space since March, but I had been so overtaken with Emily, and her journey through the Redcliff programme, and with getting hold of myself following my breakdown, that I felt that I was only just beginning to appreciate the space. I wondered how long Jonathan could hold on. Was it reasonable to expect him to, or should I just let him go?

By the time we got to Palm Springs I was very tired. I had been driving for more than eight hours and, in spite of the rest stops, the constant glare from the sun had made my eyes tired. Emily was being OK, but the thought of spending the night in some motel with her in this mood was not appealing. I decided to press on to LA where I knew we would get a warm welcome.

After Palm Springs it felt like we were in LA. We had left the desert and our route was lined with business parks, hotels, and all the trappings of the outer limits of a city. Bob had given me excellent directions and I only made one mistake – coming off the freeway at Pasadena by accident and then struggling to find my way back on. However, I finally reached familiar territory and we headed up to Calabasas. It was funny how I now felt LA to be a familiar place –over the years I had spent quite a bit of time there. Also, Tom spends far too much time on a Playstation game called 'The Streets Of LA' and I sometimes find myself forced to play or to watch him. The area represented is downtown LA and is very realistic. I can even take him to Julie and Jon's house in Moore Drive. Tom once staged an elaborate 'gang bust' outside her house!

By 8.00 pm we reached Calabasas Hills and the guard at the gate, who now recognised me, waved us through. We had been on the road for eleven and a half hours and I was beat. Janette, Bob and Alyse were all there, and greeted us with wild whoops of joy. Alyse immediately jumped on the phone to arrange to take Emily out for a reunion with Matt and her friends. I was reeling from the drive – in fact I had the weirdest sensation of still moving! But I was so glad to be there.

That night Emily slept with me. She had had a great evening seeing everyone and swapping stories with Matt about their wilderness experiences. Now she was tired from the journey, but we both had trouble sleeping, so we just talked for ages until eventually our brains switched off.

## 23rd August – LOS ANGELES

Today was a great day. I got on the phone and made arrangements to visit Julie, as well as my wonderful aunt and uncle, Valerie, in Laguna Nigel, on the coast just south of LA. It was also the last night before David (Janette and Bob's son) went back to college in Indiana, so there was a lot of celebrating to do. Janette was fussing about his packing, while David rolled his eyes heavenwards at her loving antics. Alyse and Emily were on the computer, contacting Emily's friends back in England to tell them she was 'out' of the programme, and I lay by the pool chatting to Bob and topping up my tan.

## 24th August – LOS ANGELES

Emily and I drove down to Julie's house and spent the evening with her and her family, sitting out in their courtyard with Emily telling stories of Redcliff. It was a lovely evening listening to her and it was then that I began to wonder if we should write all this down. Julie suggested it, and Emily agreed it would be great if it could help other kids going to Redcliff. One of the most frightening things for her, she said, was going into the unknown. She honestly experienced many moments when she thought she would never get home again. She thought that her journals might help other kids and their parents.

## 25th August – LAGUNA NIGEL

We left Julie's at a time when we knew we would miss the LA morning gridlock on the freeway, and took a leisurely drive down to Laguna Nigel. This is another rather special place, a little oasis in the desert, south of Newport Beach, with its own stunning beaches.

It was wonderful to see Val, my mother's younger sister, and someone I have felt an incredible closeness to all my life, despite the fact that she has lived all over the world.

Val was great with Emily and noticed big changes in her. We all did lots and lots of talking and, as we had hoped, hit the beach for a walk in the afternoon. It was a perfect afternoon – light-hearted and silly, skipping in and out of waves and teasing each other in between exchanging all our news. Brewin, my uncle, caught up with us later on and we walked for miles together.

We went out for a Japanese meal, and all too soon it was time to go. I hate saying goodbye to Val. Because we live so far apart, I'm never certain when I will see her again.

We drove back to Calabasas along the coast road. It was longer, but more scenic. Emily and I were both in great moods and had music blasting all the way. I lost concentration and missed the turning for Topanga Canyon, so we ended up driving through the canyon in the dark, which was a pity.

## 26th August – LOS ANGELES

Our week in LA was flying by and this was our last full day. We did lots of shopping and I also managed a walk around the lake with Janette and her friends (who had all become my friends too!) I realised I was going to miss everyone very much.

Nothing I did would help me to switch off. Emily was still sleeping with me and it was like lying next to a phone charger! She practically vibrates with energy, even in her sleep – it is truly incredible. Things were now much easier between us, and we were both more relaxed and happy together. But deep down I was beginning to worry about going back to England. The nice thing about being in LA was that we could both postpone the future. We were suspended in time with our wonderful friends in 'La La Land' and from here, anything seemed possible. Going home meant hitting reality big time, and I was scared it would all go wrong.

## 27th August - HOME

We spent the morning reluctantly packing and getting ourselves organised. Luckily Janette and a few friends had organised a farewell lunch down at 'The Commons' in Calabasas, so at least we had that to look forward to. Neither of us wanted to leave.

Lunch at 'Marmalade' was fun and everyone was on good form. Emily and Alyse were very entertaining, and it was all quite loud and giggly. I then passed by the office to say goodbye to Bob, and give Janette last hugs. It was terribly hard to leave them.

They had been so good to us, and we were not able to make any definite plans about being together again.

The drive to LAX was a bit stressful. Even though we had left plenty of time to drop off the hire car and get checked in at the airport the freeway was gridlocked all the way and I even began to fear that we would miss the flight. As we struggled into the foyer they were just closing the check-in, but we made it.

Dear Virgin Atlantic! After our experiences on the way out this is now my favourite airline. Jonathan had written to them to thank them for all their help, particularly the wonderful security guard, on that terrible journey out to LA just four months ago, and we had had a very nice letter back. And now, here I was again, taking Emily home.

Although it was an overnight flight back to Heathrow neither of us slept a wink. Emily was so excited at the prospect of being home and seeing her friends again, and my mind was very unsettled. She was being quite lovely, and we chatted a lot about a much more positive future together. In spite of the rocky moments since leaving Redcliff Ascent I felt that perhaps things really had the potential for change. Maybe in years to come we would be able to look back at this moment as a turning point after all.

This girl of mine has so much to offer the world that I cannot help but believe that it will all come together for her eventually. She is beautiful and has a handful of talents, more than a lot of people have. She is charming and funny, and other people are always affected by her charisma. I accept that she has been a bloody difficult child to bring up, but there is no doubt in my mind that there is something special about her. Something different, unusual even. I was certain that things were not going to be easy from now on, but I really felt that she might finally be able to win through. She has come so far from the girl who boarded the plane in London on 24th April, four months before. Damaged by low self-esteem and self-destruction she had been so lost and angry at the world that no one could reach her anymore, especially her parents, who loved her in spite of everything. She was blind to our love then and cut off from all reason. We had done everything we could to save her and Redcliff Ascent had been our last resort.

While Emily went the distance in Utah, I had made my own personal journey. After all the nights of darkness and despair, I had somehow managed to step back from the edge, and started to rebuild myself and my life. From a journey through books, Internet, therapy, acupuncture and constant soul searching I had regained my sense of self. And with the support of my friends and family, who had stood by me all the way.

But then there was Jonathan. I truly felt that if there was a way of saving our relationship and our marriage I was going to take it, but that I was not yet ready. The dust needed to settle. I wanted to get my feet firmly on the ground before I could take that step honestly and sincerely. It had all been too awful and we had been unable to find anyone who understood what we were going through who could help us. Our impotence had almost suffocated our relationship. But maybe we had both grown through this and could now begin to weave the threads back together. Time. We needed time, and space, and calm.

The night passed and all too soon Emily was wriggling about in anticipation of breakfast. The dawn broke above the clouds and the sky was pink and clear. Slowly those on the plane who had been able to sleep began to stir and the little boys across the aisle needed Emily to help them with their computer games. Once again I had the feeling of being lost in the surreal. No one on the plane knew our story, how we came to be there. We simply looked like any mother and her daughter returning from a summer holiday in Los Angeles. I wished that we were.

We walked out through 'Arrivals' at Heathrow, but there was no sign of Jonathan and Tom. I wished we were in a movie; a warm and loving family reunion in the midst of all the chaos of a busy international airport terminal would have left the audience in no doubt of a happy ending. That this family would then go home to start life afresh – adventure over, all the pain and hardship resolved and each of the characters understood and forgiven for the parts they had played. But this was not a movie, but real life, and I had no control over the script.

I went outside to call Jonathan's mobile and, in doing so, missed Emily's reunion with Tom. Jonathan found me outside on the pavement while other passengers, leaving and arriving, surged around me on that dull, cloudy, end-of-summer morning. I was glad to be going home and wished, with all my heart, that sometime soon I would be able to reflect on these events and realise that this terrible journey had been worth taking.

# Epilogue – Beyond the Bounds of Reason

Emily, like me, has always loved the poems of Emily Dickinson and I felt very emotional when I discovered this one written on the cover of her last journal at Redcliff Ascent – it was always one of my favourites and something we shared together when she was little and we were living in Washington.

*If I can stop one heart from breaking,*
*I shall not live in vain;*
*If I can ease one life the aching,*
*Or cool one pain,*
*Or help one fainting robin*
*Unto his nest again,*
*I shall not live in vain.*

I wish I could say that we all lived happily ever after. But we didn't.

Things started well at St Mary's. Emily seemed to settle down and make friends quickly. She fell in love with photography, and feedback from her teachers indicated that she was doing well academically, she had A grades in three subjects and a sprinkling of B grades. Not at all bad for someone who had been out of education for a year.

However, by half term things were coming unstuck and Emily dive-bombed. She made connections with boys at the local comprehensive school and started to go missing – particularly at night. She became extremely challenging to her teachers and was divisive and bullying among her peers. After she went missing one evening, and staff and dogs had combed the grounds in the middle of the night searching for her, the school had had enough. After less than three months Emily was expelled from her new school for outrageous behaviour.

After expulsions from three schools we could not find another school willing to take her. Even with the support of our Member of Parliament, who was very sympathetic and worked quite hard on our behalf, the local education authority could not be persuaded to provide any alternative education programme for her. This bright, intelligent and gifted child has thus had no formal education beyond the age of fourteen, in spite of attending three of the best schools in the country. She has no qualifications and no prospects, and she does not care.

While I dared to hope that St Mary's would work out for Emily, I started to write. Once I began, the story poured out, and I became an extension of my computer day and night until the tale was told. It began as a process of catharsis – I was desperate to unload all that had happened in order to move on. As the pages multiplied I began to realise that it was becoming a story that others might like to read and that maybe it could even offer some support and guidance to parents who find themselves engaged in similar wars with their teenagers.

One autumn weekend Jonathan, home from Manchester and sleepless on the Saturday night, read the raw manuscript and went ballistic, ranting and raving at me in the middle of the night while I pretended to be asleep. As I lay and listened to him, his abuse and his threats, I realised that the love I once had for this man was irretrievable. He then set about taking the manuscript to pieces and his amendments – huge tracts of red text – blotted out my story.

The next day was stormy and I felt angry that once again he had totally undermined my attempts to find my own voice in this family.

Jonathan left for Manchester on Sunday evening and I sat down to compose a final letter to him, ending our marriage.

Jonathan lost his job the following day and, while my letter hovered in the postal system, irretrievable but not yet received, I came unstuck, and did not resist when he packed up his life in Manchester and came to live at home again. The letter arrived the following morning and was put aside. He told me he had decided to ignore it. I was distraught, but felt I had no choice but to carry on as before, as if all my thinking and decision-making had been irrelevant, totally inconsequential. I was thoroughly deflated. Once more overtaken by events and without any control over what was happening.

Our efforts at yet again trying to pull our marriage back together were soon a miserable failure. I gradually shut down emotionally and fell into a phase of simply existing from day to day. In my head I was trying to survive, in my heart I was without hope. While Emily drifted back into a life of drugs and running away, Jonathan and my relationship disintegrated and eventually, the following summer, we began the always-acrimonious process of divorce.

Meanwhile, Emily's behaviour was escalating out of control. She began a relationship with a guy who dealt drugs and she was soon stoned most of the time. Her violent rages returned and Jonathan threw her out of the house. At this time I had moved out of the family home with Tom and we were living in a rented house in Wimbledon. Emily's behaviour was so destructive that I felt I needed to protect us and so kept our new address a secret from her. However, we spoke on a daily basis and I tried to meet up with her as often as possible. Sometimes she would turn up as arranged, sometimes not. Often she made no sense at all but it was clear from her damaged knuckles (she took to 'beating up alleyways when she got mad') that she was suffering extreme angst and pain. I could do nothing to help her. During this time she was living with a girlfriend and sleeping on the floor, surrounded by her belongings in black plastic bags.

On July 6<sup>th</sup> she turned sixteen. Jonathan and I took her out to celebrate but it was a disaster. She could not cope with being in a restaurant and became so agitated and panicky that she left the meal and I had to sit outside with her. We went to a birthday party the following evening at the house where she was living. It was an extremely hostile occasion where I met her boyfriend, and a few of her friends over cake and wine. Jonathan left quickly but I stayed, punishing myself with the sheer tragedy of the situation as she smoked two huge joints in front of me and disappeared into another galaxy. Her view was that now she was sixteen she could do what she liked. She did not even say goodbye. Her friends seemed to admire her independence and applaud her outrageous behaviour.

This 'coming of age' had serious repercussions with trying to get help for Emily. Suddenly she was allowed to make her own decisions about her life – whether or not to take medication, whether to cooperate with the Community Adolescent Mental Health Team, which was currently responsible for trying to help her. She could now invoke the adult privilege of 'confidentiality', making it impossible for us to keep hold of what was happening, and leaving us powerless either to guide these professionals or to support her. Emily began to refuse all intervention, choosing a path of self-destruction and sabotage.

One morning in July, I received a call from her friend that Emily had 'totally lost it' and had gone missing. Her friends and boyfriend had been out looking for her since early morning and were clearly terrified as to what she might do. While I joined a frantic search for her, she called Jonathan. Although she was totally incoherent he managed to work out where she was and I joined him there within minutes. We found her walking into the traffic near the A3, ranting and raving. She had no idea where she was, or even who she was. She was like a wild animal on the rampage. Between us we managed to wrestle her into the car and rushed her to A&E at Kingston Hospital. The place was packed and we had no means of controlling her. As she ricocheted around the reception area shouting abuse, security was called and we were taken through to what I hoped would finally be some real help. Nothing she did or said made any sense at all – it was as if she had gone totally mad. She refused to cooperate until her father left the hospital and once she was convinced he had gone she accused him of abusing her. It was devastating to see her like this.

Emily was suffering from a drug-induced psychosis and many hours later was 'sectioned' to be detained in a secure unit under the Mental Health Act. In the early hours of the morning we went with her by ambulance to Springfield Psychiatric Hospital in Wandsworth. For more than two weeks she had no idea of who she was or what was happening to her. She thrashed around in a total fury, sometimes restrained in a padded room, raging at the world. She had to have twenty-four hour care and security during this time as she made attempts to throw herself out of the (barred) window and to escape – she could not be left alone for a second. Jonathan and I were terrified that she would never regain her sense of reality. In a way she did, but her reality is not one that we can share.

Visiting her was traumatic – you could never be sure what would happen next. Her favourite trick was setting off the alarms, causing total chaos on the ward as the staff reacted to the 'emergency'. However, gradually, the anti-psychotic medication and the careful handling of the staff started to work their magic. By the end of the summer she was stable enough to go home.

And still the cycles of calm and chaos remain. In a calm phase we get a glimpse of the wonderful person that Emily can be, and then she slides into chaos and the violence and rage returns. The worst thing is having to come to terms with the fact that I can no longer have any influence over her life. No one can. She must now help herself, and until she does, she continues to live in a sort of twilight world parallel to, but not a part of, reality. Omnipotent but vulnerable.

Now, eighteen months after the airport reunion, the family home is up for sale. Tom and I are preparing to move to a new home and a new start, Jonathan is going his own way, and Emily is out there somewhere. She is still railing against the world but is now way beyond our help. When they find her, the police will arrest her for criminal damage to her home - an Easter visit that ended with her trying to smash her way into the house, and I will have to decide whether or not to prosecute my own daughter.

Emily hates me with every fibre of her being. The more I have tried to help her the more she has tried to sabotage my efforts. It has become some sort of elaborate game to her. Worst of all, she thinks it is funny and is determined to win.

In spite of everything, I still have a daughter, and I do love her. But I can't keep hoping that everything will be all right, because it never is. It doesn't matter how many mountains I climb, if Emily will do nothing to help herself then I can't do it for her. I need to move on and make something of my own life – build a new home with Tom and our dog, Harry, and start living again. For too many years I have allowed Emily to totally consume me – and for what?

I have had to work very hard to keep myself from being pulled back into her chaotic world. That would be a path of self-destruction for me, and I cannot go there, for Tom's sake, as well as my own. Throughout this long and painful journey, although I have frequently been pushed beyond my limits, physically and emotionally, I have gained a new strength and resilience and now I must build on that. I have also learned not to try to cope with this all alone, but to take the help so frequently offered by my family and friends, and to pursue other ways of taking care of myself.

This goes against a mother's natural instinct to care for her children, before herself. In my case this instinct got out of proportion, but sometimes (often) I feel as if I am now being selfish – how can I expect to be happy when my daughter is in so much pain? Yet I know that taking on her pain does nothing for her, and just destroys my spirit.

I know now that all I can do for Emily at the moment is to never lose faith in her. I need to try to keep the door ajar until she is able to commit to changing her life, and I hope then that she will have enough confidence in our love to find her way back to her family.

Maybe one day she will turn up at the door and will be able to show me that she has changed, and is willing to give our relationship another go. And I will be overjoyed and will welcome her with open arms, my Prodigal Daughter, 'Laughing Star'.

We hope you enjoyed reading this book;

Please do feel free to get in touch and let us know your comments.
reviews@discoveredauthors.co.uk

Undiscovered Authors is a national writing competition searching out literary talent.

www.undiscoveredauthors.co.uk

This new initiative from Discovered Authors aims to help exciting, original works by talented authors get the bookshelf space and readership they deserve.

Please turn the page to find out more about our Undiscovered Authors winning titles to be published in 2006 and to learn more about our other authors and browse our online bookshelves please visit:

www.discoveredauthors.co.uk

*Discovered Authors*
*50 Albemarle Street*
*Mayfair, London*
*W1S 4BD*

Other Undiscovered Authors competition winning titles published in 2006 include:

### *The Tale of Findo Gask* by Huw Thomas
**National Winner of the 2005 Undiscovered Authors Fiction Competition.**
*The Tale of Findo Gask* tells the story of a thief, born in a ditch, raised in slums and educated by the underworld. An unregistered child with no official identity, Findo begins to steal in order to survive, but his exploits soon become more audacious...
This is not a crime novel, but the story of an unconventional life; of alienation, love and a desperate search for acceptance.

### *Sentinel* by Tony O'Reilly
**Winner of the Undiscovered Authors 2005 National Prize for Ireland.**
After a viral artificial intelligence is accidentally created, a chain of events begin to unfold which promise to bring chaos to society. Spanning the Middle East, France, Spain and Ireland, Sentinel follows the journey of three strangers as they join together in a last desperate attempt to fight the seemingly unstoppable life force... but the final confrontation leads to a truth more terrifying and far-reaching than they could ever have thought possible.

### *Struggling Free* by Margaret Penfold
**Regional Winner for Undiscovered Authors 2005**
When conflicts and contradictions in Palestine during the British Mandate lead to the deaths of a Syrian property owner and a British police inspector, three women watch the events unfold.
*Struggling Free* follows Patsy, Dalia and Suzanna- three young women from very different backgrounds- as they unite through their trials of love, murder and war.
Margaret Penfold, spent her formative years in Palestine, and her experiences as a child inspired her to write a fictional account of the struggle she witnessed.

All Discovered Authors titles are available to buy at
www.amazon.co.uk and all good bookshops.